No Sex In The City

Teresa Smith

Dedicated to all of the single women who are waiting on the one who is “perfect” for you.

To my children, Demetrius and Malcolm-
you always make me laugh.
To my grandchildren, Avery and Jeremiah-
you have my heart.
To all of my family and friends-
your unfailing support amazes me.

Disclaimer

This is a work of fiction. Names, characters, events and incidents are the products of the author's imagination. Although there are people who carry these names, none of the people are real. Any resemblance to actual persons, living or dead, or actual events is purely coincidental.

INTRODUCTION

It has been five years since my failed marriage and divorce. I have not allowed my experience with Derek to stop me from dating. I am going to be "woke" this time around. Any sign of a personality disorder, narcissism, emotional unavailability or abuse; I am going to run and run fast. Dating used to be so easy. A guy or girl would write a note. Do you like me yes or no? Or a brave young man would ask a girl if she would like to go steady? Dating was as simple as walking up to a girl, asking her out and boom…. y'all go together. That courtship lasted throughout high school, college and til death did them part for some. I remember someone saying men are like buses, if you miss one catch the next one. That was thirty years ago. Currently, men are like a great magic act. Now you see me-Now you don't.

The Bible was written thousands of years ago, but it rings true today. "In that day so few men will be left that seven women will fight for each man saying, let us all marry you! We will provide our own food and clothing. Only let us take your name so we won't be mocked as old maids" (Isaiah 4:1). I do not know whether or not scripture was prophesying a man shortage. Things that make me go hmmmm. Are many of us abstaining from sex because we are sold out to Christ? Or are many of us abstaining because there are not a lot of eligible men to choose from? It could be both.

At the insistence of friends, I have begun my quest to date. At this rate, I'm inclined to believe that there is absolutely no sex in the city.

According to the Census Bureau there were 161 million females in the United States in 2013 versus 156.1 million males. There are five million more women in the United States than men. Nationally, women make up 50.8 percent of the population, but that percentage varies across states. District of Columbia has the highest percentage of females at 52.8 percent followed by Rhode Island at 51.7 percent and Maryland at 51.6 percent. On the other hand, Alaska has the lowest percentage of females at 48.0 percent followed by Wyoming at 49.0 percent and North Dakota at 49.5 percent.

There are only nine states where males make up more than 50 percent of the population: Alaska, Colorado, Hawaii, Idaho, Montana, Nevada, North Dakota, Utah and Wyoming. That is freaking amazing. Unfortunately, I do not know anyone who lives in any of those places. Let's see. I live in the great state of Texas where the slogan is everything is bigger, including gender ratios. The total population of Texas is estimated at 53, 913, 916 people with 26, 764, 772 male and 27, 149, 144 females. There are 384, 372 more women than men in the state, which is 0.71% of the total population. Women outnumber men which makes it difficult to date.

In the television series Sex and The City, Carrie Bradshaw never had problems finding a date nor getting laid. As a matter of fact, Carrie, Samantha, Charlotte and Miranda played a man's game. Well, Charlotte was the marrying kind. The others would meet a guy and slay a guy. I mean get laid with a guy. Although dating is not solely about having sex, it is about going out on dates and being courted. What happened to good old-fashioned courting? Sheriff Andy Griffith and Helen used to date. He courted Helen. They sat on the porch, drank sweet tea and talked. Fred Sanford and Donna used to sit on the sofa and talk. A long time ago, men pursued, loved and respected women. Dating has become a lost art. Most men and women go from hello to the bedroom. They go from the restaurant to the bedroom, and from the bar to the backseat. Unlimited access to sexually lucid women has made it difficult for people with standards/values to settle down or even get married. Culture says let's live together before we get married. Kingdom says marriage is honorable.

Chapter 1

Due to our new sexual revolution, wholesome women are sitting in their homes wondering "*what in the high heavens is going on*?" Seriously, why would a man wait? A high number of sexually active women and men are getting married but those who are abstaining cannot buy a date. So many people no longer believe in waiting to have sex after marriage. It is sex, children and then marriage. My point is sex has consumed many. The flesh wants what it wants. Let's face it. Sex satisfies the flesh. So many women are fasting, sowing, praying, believing and waiting for a husband. Many women who are "sexually free" are not waiting but are getting married. Many of us who are abstaining are saying "What about me Lord?" If there are seven women to one man, there are five out of those seven women who aren't waiting to have sex so who are these men going to marry? Certainly not you or me. Single women have gotten creative with why it is taking so long to get married. Some will say it is in God's timing. Others will say I am better off single. A few will say they are working on their careers or education. The last group will say they are not ready. I almost forgot. I have met women who have stated they need a husband who can carry them in the spirit. Whatever that means. But I wonder if all of these excuses are due to past hurts or a shortage of eligible men? Or is it fear of getting married and divorced? Or is it something we tell ourselves because it has not happened yet? If I had an answer, I would be a billionaire. We are sexual beings; therefore, many of us desire sex. God's words tell us to wait, but society tells us to test drive the car before buying it.

Sex was concealed a lot more back in the day or shall I say it was more subtle. In the movies and television shows, married folks did not promote sex. I remember watching shows like "I Love

Lucy." Lucy and Ricky slept in separate beds I and was confused when Lucy became pregnant. George and Louise kissed and hugged but they were rarely filmed in the bedroom. Think about it. Mr. and Mrs. Cunningham (Happy Days), Archie and Edith (Archie Bunker) and Florida and James Evans (Good Times) showed subtle forms of affection. Sexuality was not oozing off the screen. Jimmie "JJ" Walker and The Fonz were playboys but I cannot remember one episode where I saw them feeling up a woman or taking her to bed. I wonder when our attitudes towards sexuality changed.

I'm not saying sex and pornography are new. Hugh Hefner published Playboy in 1953 with Marilyn Monroe on the cover. Larry Flint published Hustler in 1974. In 1970, it is estimated hardcore porn generated approximately $10 million. In 1998, porn revenue had increased to $750 million to $1 billion. Fast forward to 2014, pornography brought in more than $13 billion on a yearly basis in the United States alone. I can't imagine what those numbers are like now in lieu of modern technology. We were not as hot and horny because we only had three channels. They say you are what you watch and to be careful about what enters your eye and ear gates. Sex is on commercials. Women have full blown orgasms while shampooing their hair. Sexual innuendos are in every movie, commercial, magazine, television shows and cartoons.

We are sex crazy because sex is everywhere. It takes self-control in order to contain that flesh. Sex has replaced dating. If you look in the dating dictionary dating equates to sex. Ask anyone who has gone out on a date. What did you do on your date? No lie. My acquaintances have shared with me that they went to dinner, hotel and sex. We talked on the phone for hours and afterwards we had sex. That was the second date. We are practically married so we had sex. Three months is a long-term relationship for most people. In 2009, Steve Harvey's book "*Act Like a Lady and Think Like a Man*" suggests women wait for three months before giving up the cookie. He refers to it as the 90-day rule. I watched Steve's interview on Oprah.Steve said something like it takes 90 days before your benefit package kicks in on a new job so why not make a man earn the benefits. Let me find the exact quote in his book. Steve Harvey wrote, "So if Ford and the government won't give a man benefits until he's been on the job and proven himself, why, ladies, are you passing out benefits to men before they've proven themselves worthy?" Since Steve Harvey is the self-proclaimed love guru, many women followed his advice. I'm not judging because that is your business. Technically, three months is not a long time to wait. Dating and sex can become a vicious cycle. Wait the three months, give up the cookie, he leaves, and the process starts all over again. Sheesh! What does a woman have to do in order to be courted? Times were so simple when all a man wanted was to hold a woman's hand and kiss her on the cheek. He may have wanted sex, but he practiced self-control. Those were the good old days. If a woman wants to be courted, there is a strong possibility she is single and waiting. She is waiting on this man who probably does not exist. She is waiting on this man ministers are preaching about. He is going to love God, Jesus and her. He is going to wait until they get married before making sexual advances.

According to most sermons, he is going to wait for marriage before consummating. I would love it if that were true for all people. We are imperfect people living in an imperfect world. The more I talk to married couples who are Christians; some of them reveal they actually did not wait until their wedding night. It is the message they choose to tell in order to look holy and to spare someone from the hell they went through because of disobedience. Are we too far gone? Are there men who are willing to wait to consummate their marriage on their wedding night? Is it too late to get back to the basics? I do believe there are some abstinent and faithful men. Where are they and why aren't they pursuing abstinent and faithful women? Or are these people who are waiting satisfying flesh by masturbation, oral sex and sex toys? Maybe the ultimate goal isn't marriage anymore. Maybe the goal is to prove who can go without sex the longest. If no one is having sex, how do we populate the earth? Isn't being fruitful and multiplying a part of God's plan for our lives? If so, why are we hiding from love and marriage? In order to get to the institution of marriage, we have to date. As a Christian, if you mention the word dating people immediately start giving unsolicited advice, especially married women.

"You better be careful"

"It's probably not time yet"

"If I was single, I would focus on Jesus alone"

"I would take the time to get to know myself"

"It is good to be alone. You don't have to answer to anyone"

"I can come and go as I please"

"It is peaceful when you are alone"

"Honey, if this one leaves, I will never get married again"

"Single women are thirsty"

"You are making marriage an idol"

Were you thirsty before you get married? If you are that miserable, how come you have not left? The advice is never ending. I have never met a married man or woman that talks about marriage being beautiful and a blessing from God. It is always doom and gloom. One half of me laughs and the other half of me is saddened. People mean well but.......................!

Chapter 2

I moved from Oklahoma City to Fort Worth, TX. I'm starting over yet again. It has been five years since my divorce. I have prayed, fasted, sowed and repented. I repented for getting married and divorced twice. Did I feel like a failure? Absolutely. I recognized that I have to start making better choices. I have read all of the self-help books and even engaged in counseling. I have meditated and reflected on the type of men I tend to attract. Everyone has advice about why a woman is single. The women will say "you should have done this or that," "you have to talk to a man this way or that way," "you have to let him sow his wild oats." All of the responsibility falls on the woman. We are blamed for who we attract or whether or not we can keep the man. I cannot and will not accept this rhetoric that I am responsible for the type of men I attract. I agree with Dr. Aesha, "We cannot be responsible for the type of men we are attract, but we are responsible for the type of men we entertain. We choose a man based on the type of love we think we deserve"-Dr. Aesha. OUCH! That stung. I have to continue doing the work because I have settled more often than not.

Here is the deal. I'm 52 and fabulous. I'm saved, sanctified, and Holy Ghost filled. I am gainfully employed. I continue to reinvent myself by studying and learning. I am Lisa, Woman of God. I borrowed that line from the Book of Ruth. With all that I am, it has taken me this long to learn to love myself. I did not realize that I did not completely love myself. You will know that you do not completely love yourself by what you accept. I have accepted a lot of stuff from men and women. Once you learn to love yourself, you will no longer be a doormat. Women can attract a man seven days a week when we are wounded or broken. Those men will see how you devalue yourself and you will become their prey. I have been chewed up and spit out by a couple of guys. I never want to experience that type of disappointment ever again. I don't want a man to subtract from my life. He must be an addition. I saw a post on Facebook that said, "A man can look good and fullfill your fleshly desire, but he can be deadly to your soul." I have made some deadly connections, to include both ex-husbands and a couple of situationships. We won't talk about those. Instead, let's talk about my current dating situation or lack thereof.

I work in Social Services which is extremely time consuming. This job is more demanding than I would like. If you are not careful, it becomes your god. Most of my coworkers are single or divorced. I'm almost positive the demands of the job have contributed to their fate. The work itself kind of forces you into this abyss. You have to make the time to self-care and find balance. You have to choose to put yourself and your family first. After-all, you cannot pour from an empty cup. However, this line of work will steal all of your virtue if you allow it. I have spent more time on case notes than in prayer. I have spent more time in the homes of families than in church. The demands of this job keep you so busy that by the time you look up you are 65-years - old, retired and alone. More women work social services because we are natural born caregivers and nurtures. We have been trained to think we can "fix" people. We end up in professions that match our personalities. Here I am "a fixer" of other people's problems. We are expected to get to the root of other people's relationship problems while ours go unattended. We offer solutions on how to treat each other, give them direction, and provide parenting advice. We are unlicensed mental health professionals or wounded angels. Unfortunately, the system nor the families view us as humans with problems. I don't know about them, but I would like to come home to a husband. I would like someone to talk to after a bad at work. If I may be honest, I get tired of "solving other people's problems" or putting a band aid on their problems but I go home alone. At least they have each other. One of my coworkers said at least we go home in peace. That may be a true statement; however, I still believe two are better than one. "Two are better than one, because they have a good return for their labor; if either of them falls down, one can help the other up. But pity anyone who falls and has no one to help them up. Also, if two lay down together, they will keep warm. But how can one keep warm alone? Though one be overpowered, two can defend themselves. A cord of three strands is not quickly broken." (Ecclesiastes 4:9-12 NIV)

I hear women say that they are satisfied with only Jesus. Sometimes I feel guilty for desiring a husband because I feel like I am saying Jesus isn't enough. Didn't God give me the desire for a husband? Although I feel guilty, I must be honest. I want God, Jesus, The Holy Spirit, and a husband. There, I said it and I will continue to stand in my truth. I will not allow anyone to make me feel guilty because that is my desire. A desire for a spouse is normal and natural.

One day at the office, a group of us were talking about relationships. Of course, I was questioned about my singleness. I shrugged my shoulders because I did not have any answers to that question. One of my coworkers asked if I had tried internet dating, which I had briefly in the past. I'd created a profile but deleted it quickly. I felt ashamed and guilty. Why would I want to meet a man online?

Tara said, "I set up a profile on Plenty of Fish. I have met some nice guys and some not so nice guys. I have traveled to meet the guys."

I heard the word "travel" and honed in on it.

"You traveled to meet a stranger. You weren't not afraid he was the killer?" I inquired.

Everyone laughed.

I am addicted to the ID Channel (Investigation Discovery). I love "Lt Joe Kenda Homicide Hunter" "Deadly Women" and "Fatal Vows". On TV One, you will find me watching "For My Man" and "Fatal Attraction." In my mind I am learning how to identify serial killers, stalkers and abusers. They laughed but I was serious. After watching those shows, you come to realize people are sick and twisted.

"I conduct background checks on everyone before meeting them." Tara explained.

Rene shared, "You have to conduct background checks these days. There are too may criminals, domestic abusers, and men who molest children."

I frowned. "I met my friend of three years on Plenty of Fish," said Rene. "He is really nice."

Tara and Rene encouraged me to give it a try. I pondered. I justified. I made excuses but did not create the profile. I was not afraid of creating the profile. I was afraid of the rejection and not meeting a quality man. I feel like the men are hiding behind the computer and creating these false identities. I know women are doing it too. However, I am not trying to meet a woman. I am tired of meeting representatives. Men present this false front, but the real person will eventually surface. Oftentimes, we fall for the representative. How honest are internet daters? How honest is anyone for that matter. Lying, manipulation and lack of accountability are the three adjectives that describe most men. Internet dating will only fuel the ego. Men can connect with women who would not give them the time of day in person. You do not have to leave the house in order to meet anyone. You can have emotional relationships with multiple people without leaving your home. Even Steve Urkle can feel like Denzel Washington behind the computer screen.

I rationalized and justified. How bad could it be? I married an Elder from the church. He was mean, wounded and unfaithful. From the pulpit to the pew, grocery store, gym, educated/uneducated, employed/unemployed, believers and non-believers of the male species were beginning to look and act the same.

On the flip side, I have met a few couples who met online and have successful marriages. Everything is contingent upon the person, regardless of where you meet him. Weeks went by and Tara asked if I had created a profile.

"No ma'am. I am scared and tired. I am tired of starting over."

"Look, you are one of the most intuitive people I know. Listen to your intuition and have fun. You are not going to meet anyone going from work, church, the movies and home. I think you are a great woman and deserve to have someone." Tara continued, "I am enjoying boo right now. I am nervous but so far so good. Take a chance."

After work, I went home and stared at the computer. *Should I or should I not? Do it? Just do it. What can it hurt?* I researched the best dating sites. I set up a profile on Christian Mingle and InterracialDating.com. One is free and the other is a small fee for thirty days.

Profile: I am 5'9" average build, Christian, educated, divorced, two adult children and do not want anymore, drinks socially, looking for long term dating or marriage. Serious inquiries only. I chose a profile picture that was not sexy. I chose ***LovelyLady*** as my internet name.

I grabbed my journal and wrote, 'Today is October 1, 2017, and this is my dating chronicle. I don't know where this is going but I am going to give it a try. I texted Tara and said, "Done." She replied with a thumbs up. I checked both sites the next day and to my surprise there were several hits. I responded to a few guys. I always check height and the number of children first. Due to my current career, I cannot date a man with small children. I will not date a man with small children or children under the age of 18 years old. I am not dealing with baby mama drama nor child support. I'm a tall chick and I am not interested in men under 6'. I'm not compromising in that area. I'm 6' with heels. I do not need or want a man with a Napoleon complex in my life. I do not need anyone to feel inferior to me because of his shortcomings.

This guy looks interesting. His profile name was *ChosenOne.* Hi, I am a Minister of the Gospel of Jesus Christ. I pastor a small church in Lewisville, TX. Divorced with two children over 18. Self-employed and looking for a wife who is faithful to God and has her own goals and dreams. I rolled my eyes because ministers have access to plenty of women. I wonder what could possibly be his problem . I wonder if he has slept with some of the women in his church and now, he has to look outside of his church. We shared a conversation in the chat room and eventually exchanged numbers. Of course, he immediately asked for a picture. I sent him a picture. I requested a picture as well. He sent a picture, but it was blurry. I requested another picture. He sent a picture wearing sunglasses. I requested a picture where I could see his eyes. He claimed that he did not have any more pictures. I was not pleased. What are you hiding sucka? I do not like him. I blocked and deleted his number and profile. In my mind, he is hiding something.

Several men reached out to me. Mainly offering me a good time if I wanted to meet and you know what the good time meant…..sex. No dinner, lunch nor movie. No getting to know me, only sex. That was very disappointing. None of my pictures displayed sexiness. I'm getting so tired of Black men. I love them but I am worried about their mental wellness and state of maturation. I know the average man equates sex with love, but there is something going on with my brothers. There is a lack of foundation and stability amongst a lot of Black men. I am concerned because there is a disconnect between Black men and women. I believe it began in slavery, but I do not want to do a history lesson right now. I have decided I am going to date white men only. I am going to position myself in order to meet a successful white man. I am not saying white men are better than Black men, but white men do find my beauty more appealing. They compliment me more and appear to have some interest in me. Who am I kidding? Can I handle the stress of an interracial relationship? I tend to think of most white men as narcissistic and arrogant. I just don't know if I am ready for that. I am not against it, but I do not know if I am quite ready. I do not want to give up on my brothers, but they play too much. I have never been afraid of a challenge or failing. Let me focus on this other site.

While on InterracialDating.com, more Black men reached out to me than white men. A few of them had the nerve to ask why a fine Black woman was on an interracial dating site. What in the double standard is going on? Your Black behind is on a dating site looking for Asian, Hispanic and White women. I do not understand. I was really confused at how condescending some of these brothers were towards my interest in white men. I will never figure that one out. You cannot keep the average Black man from playing in snow but they have the audacity to get an attitude when we went to go skiing too. I chatted with several Black men but the conversation led to sex. I'm positive they were seeking sex from the White, Hispanic and Asian women as well. They were not interested in meeting unless it was for sex. I began blocking and deleting. This is not going well at all. This is outright boring.

Tara and Rene asked, "How is it going?

"It is not going well at all. I specifically asked for men 6' and over but men 5'3" to 5'11" keep reaching out to me. Men with small children and men who live out of state keep reaching out to me. I specifically requested to meet men within the Dallas/Fort Worth area. They cannot read or they are not reading the profile."

Tara and Rene laughed. "You are a pretty woman and that is all men see."

"Heck, men want pretty, and I want tall." We shared a good laugh.

"Do not give up." Tara said. She continued "You are so positive and encouraging. A man will be happy to have you."

I said, "Will he?" At this point, I was not so sure. An alert popped up on my cell. *KingBlack* would like to meet you. I clicked on his profile. KingBlack: 6', no children, professional, does not drink, Seven Day Adventist. He is looking to meet someone. He wants to go out on dates. He wants someone he can laugh with and be himself. He wants a lady who appreciates the finer things in life. She must be educated. From his picture, he looked decent.

KingBlack: Hi LovelyLady. You sure are beautiful.

LovelyLady: Hello Sir. You are attractive as well. What brings you to a dating site? What qualities are you looking for in a potential date?

KingBlack: I work a lot and it is difficult to meet a woman. My coworkers encouraged me to join the site. Several of them have met their spouses online. I am looking for an honest woman who knows how to treat a man.

LovelyLady: Describe what treating a man looks like to you, please.

KingBlack: I want a woman that knows how to cook and clean. I want her to be my support and have my back. I want my Michelle Obama.

LovelyLady: Well, I am not the one for you. I do not like to cook. I will cook rather than starve. Men love to say they want a Michelle Obama but are not willing to be Barack Obama. Have your back, huh? Will you have her back or is it all about your needs?

KingBlack: Why are you still single?

LovelyLady: Probably because I do not cook and clean. Smile at me☺

KingBlack: That is a requirement for me. I've got to have a woman that can cook and clean.

LovelyLady: A Middle Eastern mindset in a western culture. She is out there. God bless you on your search.

Lord, I just don't know. This expectation that women are only needed in the kitchen and bedroom is misogynist. I am not going to settle for a man who puts all of this responsibility on me. I desire and expect a man who can cook and clean too. He wants me to bring home the bacon, fry it up in a pan and never let him forget he is a man. This sounds so selfish. I am doing all of this, what am I getting out of the deal? A penis? Child Boo. Is this a paradigm shift? Is this culture? Is this biblical? Whatever it is……. I do not like it.

I want a partner. I want a teammate. If I get home from work first, I will cook. If he gets home from work first, he can cook. He can clean just like me. He can do laundry too. If have to work and pay my portion in order to keep the home afloat; I expect my man to dig in his heels and help. A man is not going to lose any testosterone if he makes the bed or fries a piece of chicken. There are a lot of men who enjoy cooking. *Send one my way Lord. Thanks in advance.* I looked up to heaven and winked at God for a little extra incentive. While playing on Facebook, a video from Nicole Moore surfaced on my timeline. Nicole Moore is the creator of Love Works. She is a love coach. Nicole has earned millions of dollars helping women identify their love blocks and to position themselves in order to meet the man of their dreams. I listened to the video, and she was informative. I watched her videos on YouTube and took notes. I refuse to end up with another Derek. The thought made me shudder.

Chapter 3

On December 22, 2017, I watched a video that discussed dating in bad patterns. She discussed the old way of dating which is dating for an outcome which focuses on meeting the one. She challenged women to date for growth. Dating for growth requires you to think about what you liked about each date whether good or bad. Write down things that went well on each date. Make declarations about what you deserve and expect in a man. We have been trained to talk about what we don't want. We rarely talk about what we do want. We give more life to the things we don't want and those are the type of men who manifest. Life and death are in the power of the tongue.

Many of us have had a bad experience with men, to include our fathers. A father can nurture or damage his daughters. Wounded little girls grow up to be wounded women who are always looking for that love we never received from our fathers. That wounded little girl runs the relationship. She runs it from a place of fear, control and manipulation. How we respond to is an indication of our wounds. If we feel a man is going to abandon us, we become anxious and insecure. We tend to operate from misplaced emotions. That is when we begin to call repeatedly, text feverishly and start pacing. Where is he? Why isn't he returning my calls? I knew I couldn't trust him. As women, we are going to have to work on our emotional intelligence. Emotional intelligence is the capacity to be aware of, control, and express one's emotions, and to handle interpersonal relationships judiciously and empathetically. This is the information I gathered from Nicole's video.

Dating is scary in modern America. I am going to try dating for growth, not outcome. I am going to write down all experiences.

I am going to write down all positive aspects of my dates. I will pay attention to how the guy treats wait staff which means I will be looking to see if he is kind to me and those around me. It is very important to pay attention to how a man treats everyone. My goal is to make it past three months with a guy. The guy or I lose interest around the third month. I cannot figure out why this happens, but it does. I'm going to pay close attention to the length of time a guy sticks around.

I'm going into this dating thing with an open heart and open mind. God, cover me and protect me from the hand of the enemy. I pray I will not attract the wrong person. Help me to discern every wicked man quickly. I pray that I will not attract or entertain rapists, child abusers, domestic abusers or the killer. I cannot deal with the killer. I do not want to end up on the ID Channel or Fatal Attraction. I do not want to end up dead because I picked a demon. In Jesus Name. Amen and Amen.

I received an alert from Larry P. I clicked on Larry's profile. Ooh la la. He was Hispanic with green eyes. Oh dear, this man is gorgeous, 6' tall, widowed and works on the pipeline. He says, "I am looking for a serious relationship. I do not believe in long courtships. My wife and I married after dating for only three months and were married for ten years. I enjoyed being married. I do not like dating. Women play too many games. I want to spoil, love on my lady and treat her like she deserves to be treated. My friends say I am a sucker for love. I believe in love and think life is better with someone in it. I work hard and play hard. I like to drink beer and travel. I am not a drunk. I will do whatever needs to be done for my lady. I do require fidelity. I travel a lot for work and need a lady I can trust. If this is you, feel free to respond. I am providing my email for more effective communication. My email address is…"

I am not going to respond. The word "widow" stuck out the most. I am wondering if he is the "killer." Did he kill his wife? What happened to his wife? I have questions that need answers. I am not going to respond. I am going to wait until he reaches out to me again.

Larry P's response: Oh my freaking God. You are absolutely beautiful. I would love to meet you. I'm currently in Canada working on the pipeline. I live in Dallas, TX. I will be home the first week of February. I would love to correspond with you. Is there anything you want to know?

LovelyLady: Hi. What happened to your wife?

Larry P: She died during childbirth.

LovelyLady: Sorry for your loss.

Larry and I chatted often. We moved communication from the chat room to email.

From: Lisa Davis

To: Larry

Subject: Merry Christmas

December 22, 2017 @ 11:03PM

Hi Larry,

I hope all is well. Stay safe out there.

Lisa

From: Larry Pina

To: Lisa

Re: Merry Christmas

December 23, 2017 @ 2:03AM

My darling Lisa,

Thanks so much for reaching out to me. This makes me so happy. Merry Christmas to you as well. Do you have any plans? I am so excited. I have a good feeling about you.

Larry.

On December 25, 2017, I was contacted by Paul. Paul is Caucasian. 60 years old, divorced and no children. Paul is an executive and resides in Dallas. Paul wants someone to date and eventually marry. He likes going to the movies, plays and football. He loves the Dallas Cowboys. He says, "Feel free to contact me if interested. BTW: You are freaking gorgeous."

I stared at his profile. Paul looked every bit of 60 years old. Unfortunately, he was not good looking nor handsome. He was sort of attractive. I could tell he worked out a lot. As I looked through his profile pictures, I saw a small dog. That is a negative. I am not a pet person. I do not believe dogs belong in the house. You can do whatever you like in your house; this is my belief.

LovelyLady: Hi Paul. Thanks for reaching out.

Paul: No problem. You are beautiful.

LovelyLady: Thank you.

Paul: Why are you single? A beautiful woman like you should not be single.

LovelyLady: Beauty does not keep a man. Hence, Halle Berry, Vivica Fox, Vanessa Williams, Jennifer Lopez just to name a few. I do not have an answer for why I am single. What is your story?

Paul: I am divorced and have been for two years. We were married for fifteen years. She was ill and after she became well; she wanted to travel and be free. Sickness can bring people closer or tear them apart. We are still friends and share custody of our dog.

I'm thinking oh dear. He is for real? Shared custody of the dog, I am thoroughly entertained.

LovelyLady: I am divorced as well and looking to date. I am trying to be open and try new things. I am open to interracial dating. Have you dated Black women? Is this a fetish? Or you trying something new?

Paul: Oh no. No fetish. My ex-wife is Black. I did not seek a Black woman but that is who I fell in love with. I have only dated White women, but she took my breath away. She was beautiful like you.

LovelyLady: Interesting. How did your family adjust to your Black wife?

Paul: Believe it or not, my family liked her better than me. We are not racist if that is what you wanted to know.

LovelyLady: LOL LOL LOL. I was getting to that. I do not want to be a part of a social experiment whereas a White person dates a Black woman in order to kill her in order to steal her organs. Nor do I want to be sacrificed to the devil.

Paul: Is that what you think of White people? I hope not. I do not mean to be forward, but I would like to meet you in person. Pardon my manners. Merry Christmas. It is Christmas and meeting you will be a good gift. Can meet on Friday? In a public place and you can choose the place. I want you to be comfortable.

LovelyLady: Merry Christmas. What is your favorite color? What fun things do you like to do? What is your favorite food? When were you born?

Paul: My favorite color is Blue. I am a Cowboys fan remember. I like to go to sporting events for fun. My favorite foods are Mexican and Italian. I love Mexican food. I was born on May 2nd.

Check mate. That is what I need. I conducted a background check. No criminal results were found.

LovelyLady: Well, you do not appear to be threatening. I am googling some restaurants. We can meet between Dallas and Fort Worth. Arlington perhaps? Minus being a Cowboys fan, you seem to be okay.

I researched restaurants I have not frequented. Aha! Uncle Julio's or Chuy's. I think Chuy's in Arlington will be great.

LovelyLady: We can meet at Chuy's in Arlington. It will be a midway point and we both like Mexican food. From the pictures the margaritas look delish.

Paul: This sounds good to me. I don't get off work until 6p on Friday. I want to go home and change clothes and then I will meet you there around 8. If that is, okay?

LovelyLady: Sure.

Something told me this date would never happen. While at the office, I told Tara I had a "potential" date with Paul on Friday night. She agreed to sit at the bar for security purposes.

"What is he like?" Tara asked.

"He is White, 60, no children, divorced and lives in Dallas. His ex-wife is Black. I am not excited because I think he is going to bail." "Be positive," said Tara. "It may turn out pretty good." Tara forgot she is the one who said I am the most intuitive person she knows. I should start making bets. I would be rich by now.

Around 5pm, Tara ushered me out of the office and told me to go home and get dressed. Instead, I stopped by Redbox, Wingstop and the liquor store before heading home. I knew I was going to be in for the night. I was going to watch movies, have wings and wine. Yes indeed. I put on my pajamas, popped in a movie and made myself comfortable on my chaise. I received an alert.

Paul: I am so sorry, I will not be able to make it, I have to work late.

I laughed out loud and responded.

LovelyLady: No worries. Have a good weekend.

Paul: I am going to make it up to you. I do not like to break commitments. I feel so bad.

LovelyLady: Awe. Be safe and have a good evening. Chat with you next time.

I texted Tara to tell her the date was off. I told her thanks for her willingness to show up to the restaurant for support.

Tara: Are you in for the night?

Lisa: Yes ma'am. I stopped at the Redbox, bought wings and wine. I told you that date was not going to happen

Tara: You called it. Do not give up.

Lisa: Never will I give up, but I have to pay attention to that still small voice.

Paul and I chatted occasionally. It was all superficial, but it was conversation. Remember, I am dating for growth and not outcome. I am learning what I like and dislike.

Paul: Everyone will be off on New Year's Day. If you are off, let's meet for lunch. *LovelyLady:* Sure.

Paul: We can meet at Chuy's at Arlington's around noon.

LovelyLady: Sure.

Who am I kidding? This date is not going to happen. I watched a movie and was asleep before the clock struck midnight. I woke up, thanked God and said Happy New Year to me. I decided I was going to create a vision board today. It was cold in my apartment which means it was cold outside. I looked at my phone and it is 20 degrees. I knew Paul was going to cancel the lunch date. So, I began getting dressed in order to go to Walmart to purchase a poster board, glue, glitter and magazines. I am going to create my vision board for 2018.

An alert went off around 10:30 am.

Paul: Happy New Year Lisa. I am not going to be able to make it. It is too cold outside. I went outside for a few minutes, and it is freezing. I just want to stay inside in the warmth.

LovelyLady: Happy New Year Paul. No problem. Stay warm.

Paul: I hope you are not angry.

LovelyLady: No. I am not angry.

Paul: Yes, you are. I can tell by your response.

LovelyLady: Paul, I do not know you. There is no reason to be angry. Have a great day and enjoy the New Year.

Paul's response: I feel so bad. I feel really bad right now. You are so beautiful, and I would be honored to go out with you. I don't see how anyone can function in this type of cold.

LovelyLady: Well, I am about to run errands in the cold. It does not bother me at all. I was born in December and winter is my is my favorite season. Be blessed Paul.

Paul would not get another chance to cancel a meet and greet. I donned my hat and coat and headed to Walmart. I bought magazines, Cokes, water, Oreos, potato chips, pencils, pens and markers. I stopped by Family Dollar and bought other items I might need. I was a woman on a mission, 2018 will not be like the previous twenty-five years. I am going to write the vision and make it plain. I entered my apartment and threw all of my items unto the floor. I took off my winter apparel, turned on Pandora, grabbed my chips, cookies, Coke, sat on the floor, and went to work on my vision board. I cut and pasted pictures of Prince Harry and Meghan Markle. I was determined more than ever to get a White Boo. Prince Harry and Meghan had announced their engagement. I want to be a princess too. Dang it, I have always liked Prince Harry. Meghan beat me to him.

Seriously, I have always loved George Clooney, Keanu Reeves, Brad Pitt, Matt Damon, Ben Affleck and John Cusack. Did I say Keanu Reeves? He is my favorite. My fascination with White men increased after watching Olivia Pope and Fitzgerald “Fitz” Grant on “Scandal”. The way Fitz loved Olivia had become my obsession. Women were saying they wanted a Boaz. I want Fitz. Well, an unmarried Fitz. I do not want to be anyone’s mistress. Nevertheless, Tony Goldwyn made White men sexy, attractive and endearing. I wonder if I will meet two White men who will protect and love me like Fitz and Jake loved Olivia. That remains to be seen.

I continued working on my vision board. I posted pictures of books, a small SUV, beaches, scriptures, positive affirmations, inspirational quotes and a one-dollar bill. I am determined to build generational wealth. I want to write many books. I want to go to Paris, France. I want to see all of the beaches in the world. I want to leave an inheritance for my children and grandchildren. Every now and again I would get up and try to twerk. The only thing moving was my head. Maybe I should add dance lessons to the vision board. I burst out laughing. I completely understand why my cousin gave me the name ‘Rhythmless Nation’. I spent most of the morning responding to Happy New Year texts, working on my vision board and dancing. I rounded off my day watching Christmas movies on the Hallmark Channel.

I was pleased with my vision board. I put it on the wall in my bedroom. It would be the first thing I see when I wake up in the morning. I prepared for work, read my bible, prayed and laid down. I began to reflect on my dating life. I have never really dated. I dated briefly and got married. I really did not know what it was like to go out on dates. I want to date, not out of desperation but for the experience and out of curiosity. I want to know what it is like to go out to eat, to the movies and travel with someone of the opposite sex. I wondered what it would be like to have someone to like me and not be afraid to show it. I refuse to believe there is something wrong with me. I will not allow anyone else to make me feel like there is something wrong with me ever again.

I began wondering if God had me in isolation. Am I invisible to men and friends? I do not have many friends. I am not close to family members. I am really out here alone. What is going on here? There is something but I cannot put my finger on it. It feels like everyone I meet turns away from me. It feels like there is an invisible shield or veil that prevents anyone from seeing me. I need to get to the root of it. I refuse to be the cat lady. I do not like cats anyway. I am going to do some soul searching. I need to get free from whatever has me bound. What is hindering me from being found? Is God doing work on me? Am I in the healing room? Is there a curse on the women in my family that prevents us from being in healthy relationships or marriages? I am never to get marriage again. I have done it twice, so is that it for me? Maybe I won't get a do over? Maybe I will be single until the Lord says well done. On that note, I drifted off to sleep.

I woke up energized and refreshed. I am going to appreciate the life and career God has given me. Well, maybe not the career. I am leery about the career but okay God. I am going to TRY and trust you in the area of work. Every morning, I pray and read my bible. I refuse to start my day without thanking God for waking me up. I refuse to start my day without thanking God for being Jehovah Nissi. Plus, I have to pray for grace, strength, wisdom and guidance. Lord knows I need strength dealing with people. I need guidance and wisdom too. After communing with Abba, I do a little dance. Depending on my mood, I am cranking up Tasha Cobbs, Fred Hammond, Todd Delaney, Psalmist Raine, Nathaniel Coe or house music. Oh yes, I like gospel, some rap, country, rock & roll, jazz, and classical music. Praise & Worship sets the tone for my day.

From: Larry Pina

To: Lisa Davis

No Subject

January 2, 2018 @ 11:38 PM

Hi Lisa, how are you doing? I got the big contract I was working on, but I still have not gotten the girl of my dream. I will be glad if you reply to my email. Are you in a relationship now? If not please give me a chance. I am willing to give my all to you. I want a true and honest woman to come into my life.

Thank you

Larry

From: Lisa Davis

To: Larry Pina

No Subject

January 3, 2018 @ 12:31AM

Hi Larry,

You are inconsistent. I see the traits. I am not in a relationship, but I require consistency. Are you sure you are not in prison or another country? There is something off about you and your responses.

Lisa

From: Larry Pina

To: Lisa Davis

No Subject

January 3, 2018 @ 12:47AM

Oh yeah, I understand my inconsistency, but I have been extremely busy. LOL. I am not in prison and have never been to prison. I spend most of my time between America and Canada and that is the nature of my job. Yes, I want to give you consistency. I am 100% committed to consistency now.

Larry

From: Lisa Davis

To: Larry Pina

Subject: Happy New Year

January 3, 2018 @ 8:33AM

Congratulations on all of your success. Email me a different picture because I would like to know what you look like in the new year. I am wondering if you have changed.

Basically, I am wondering if he is the same person. Have you seen the television show "Catfish"?

From: Larry Pina

To: Lisa Davis

Re: Happy New Year

January 3, 2018 @ 9:42AM

Happy New Year to you and I still remember everything about you. I wish I was in Texas to celebrate with you. I will tell you a little more about me again. I am 6'2". I am loving and caring. I promise consistency. I want true love and I hope you want the same. I will sacrifice all for this to work. I want a life partner. I have met women who want a one-night stand. Yes. Some women want sex only. I am a relationship type of guy. I want one woman. I want a wife. Lisa, we have a lot to talk about. I like sex but can enjoy it with one woman. If you truly want the right one then 2018 will be the year for you. I am ready.

Thank you and I hope you have a wonderful day.

Larry

From: Lisa Davis

To: Larry Pina

Re: Happy New Year

January 3, 2018 @ 10:29AM

I do want a husband not a long-term boyfriend. I want to date and be courted. Most people on the site and in real time are looking for sex only. How old are your children? Mine are over 18.

From: Larry Pina

To: Lisa Davis

Re: Happy New Year

January 3, 2018 @ 11:15AM

Oh, your children are grown. I want you to know that in my family the women are the decision makers. I love to read, listen to good music, I love dancing, movies and shopping. I also love traveling.

I do a lot of traveling when I am overseas. I love going different places. I so want a wife, partner and friend. I want to take this to another level. I know this is hard to believe but I do not sleep around. Also, I do not believe in long courtships. I believe in dating and getting married. It does not take a man long to know who he wants to be with. I like being with one woman. I like having someone to come home to. I would like a picture of you. Will you send me a picture of you please? I will give you phone number. It is 555-216-7021.

Larry

I texted Larry a not so sexy picture. He responded and was pleased with the picture. Larry called and I could not understand him due to the accent. Darn, he is a real Mexican. I need a translator. Larry explained his reception is bad. His phone tends to drop calls when he is on the pipeline. I told him we should stick to email communication. He called multiple times but the calls kept dropping or the reception was not clear. Larry said he had to go to sleep and would check on me later. I was thinking he did not have to because I do not understand a word he is saying. I was not being ugly. He had a pleasant voice but his accent is thick.

From: Larry Pina

To: Lisa Davis

No Subject

January 5, 2018 @ 2:39AM

Hey babe, this morning I am awake, and I am reminded of the preciousness of life. I realized that I should express my gratitude to people in my life. I have not met you but communicating with me encourages me. I thank you. Thank you for coming into my life. I am falling for you day by day. I have the urge to see you. You are growing on me day by day. I have this image of us being happy.

You seem to be kind. I like that.

Sincerely,

Larry

From: Larry Pina

To: Lisa Davis

No Subject

January 5, 2018 @ 2:41AM

As bright as the sun shines

As bright as I see your beautiful face,

As bright as I think of you,

As you are my saving grace, early today, you came to my thought, I just want to say, That I think I may love you as I get to know you, Good morning and have a wonderful day.

From: Larry Pina

To: Lisa Davis

No Subject

January 5, 2018 @ 2:42AM

Cast off all of your worries and troubles from yesterday. Yesterday has passed. Promise yourself silently to make today a better day, now my friend a brand-new day awaits you. Turn to the day with excitement, it is a gift fully new, and one God has given to you, May all of your goals and wants be for this day set,

I wish you a spectacular day and night without regret. Good morning my friend. Have a terrific day!

I hope it is filled with love. You are a gem. To Queen Lisa from your boy Larry.

In between the emails, Larry texted and said he was going to fly into DFW and he hopes he can meet me for lunch. Larry was due to land at DFW airport on the morning of January 5th at 5:45am. I asked him to text me when his plane lands. Of course, no response.

From: Lisa Davis

To: Larry Pina

No Subject

January 5, 2018 @ 4:06AM

Larry,

Those are beautiful words, poetic even. I need more than beautiful words. I need action. I want to feel the love. I have never felt the love from a man. I feel the like and attraction. I feel the good "words". I do not feel the love. I know it is not that difficult. All of us are capable of loving someone other than ourselves. I have yet to experience love. Agape love has eluded me. I need something more. The distance and all of this extra is..................

Let's stay in the friend zone. It is okay to have a pen pal. Both of us are bored.

Lisa

From: Larry Pina

To: Lisa Davis

No Subject

January 5, 2018 @ 4:55AM

Hi Lisa, I lost my phone in the cab. I cannot call you or text you. I have deleted myself from the dating site. I have found the one. Email me so we can meet.

From: Larry Pina

To: Lisa Davis

No Subject

January 5, 2018 @ 5:00 AM

Hello. Will you message me please? I really lost my phone.

Larry

From: Larry Pina

To: Lisa Davis

No Subject

January 5, 2018 @ 5:55 AM

Hi Lisa, I know I am supposed to meet with you. I am afraid. I have a soft heart and I want to give it to you. You are a diamond, and no one wants to lose a diamond. I want you to reach out to me if possible. Can you call or text me so we can meet?

From: Lisa Davis

To: Larry Pina

No Subject

January 6, 2018 @ 10:01AM

Larry,

I was busy on yesterday. I hope you had a good day in Dallas. I pray all is well. Be safe. Have a good day. I am not sure I want to meet.

From: Larry Pina

To: Lisa Davis

No Subject

January 6, 2018 @ 11:31AM

Hey Beautiful Lisa,

You once told me that you find it hard to feel loved. Love is a tough and rewarding exercise and there is no exact formula to what defines love. You, who are loving and docile, has however difficulty in loving and being loved. The beauty of love is a mystery. When it finally happens, what comes to the light is a great facility of giving away, and when we know how to give it to ourselves, the exchange of love is healthy and sublime. Disclosing love requires art and skill, sensibility and attention. Love has to be sowed in a field of trust. Only this way it may be born, and grow, and finally bear fruits. So, you should follow the orientation that your immense heart gives you and rely your love on who loves you the most and dedicates you all the attention, concern and affection. You have to get rid of your fears, which derive from bad experiences that are long gone… After all, sooner or later it happens with everyone…. Let's build something beautiful for coloring our lives and days that are yet to come. Forget the fears and pessimistic forecasts, let's surrender to love. I have been thinking about this feeling I have in me; I think I am getting happier and even smile over little things…. You are changing my life in a way I could not imagine. I guess we should start talking about how we are going to meet. I am ready to sacrifice everything for you.

From: Lisa Davis

To: Larry Pina

No Subject

January 6, 2018 @ 6:01PM

Larry,

I just read your email for the second time. You are something special. What Hallmark scene did you write? Who am I kidding? I am enjoying the BS and that does not stand for Bachelor of Science.

From: Lisa Davis

To: Larry Pina

No Subject

January 7, 2018 @ 1:49PM

I like the thought of you Larry and I can see you are a good person. Bless your heart with your little inconsistent and unstable self.

From: Larry Pina

To: Lisa Davis

No Subject

January 9, 2018 @ 11:45AM

Hey Lisa, how are you doing? I am back in the USA for a little while on Monday.

I did not hear from Larry again until January 18, 2018. I did not respond to his phone call or texts. Out of the blue he called and emailed me to ask my permission to go out for drinks. He is funny. We have not been communicating nor have we met but he wants me to know he is going out for beer with his coworkers. I realized Larry never told me the age of his child. I called Larry and inquired about the age of his child. Larry said, "My daughter is 3." My eyes became as big as golf balls. "Three years old and you are 50. Your daughter is 1, 2, 3 years old as in under 5 years old? My world, why does a 50-year-old have a three-year-old? Who watches her? Oh dear. That does not seem right. Do you but oh no. I am not trying to babysit."

"My mother watches her. I don't know what I would do without my mother. I am looking for her a mother." He made that comment without a second thought. I felt like someone punched me in the stomach. I am not interested in dating a guy with small children. I don't care how cute he is. I'm getting ready to run.

Larry continued, "I am financially secure. I earn well over six figures. I am near millionaire status and this new contract has put me at millionaire status. I am opening a Mexican style restaurant in Dallas. I own my home. I want a wife and a mother for my child. You look like someone I can share my life with. You won't have to pay a bill. You can work or not."

All I could see was a 3-year-old daughter who would need a lot of attention. I am a grandmother now young enough to travel. I am not tied to anything or anyone I had so many thoughts running through my head. This is not something I am willing to do. I am currently employed in Social Services. In Texas, people call Social Services before they call on Jesus. School personnel, Law Enforcement, Medical personnel, family members, neighbors and friends call Social Services under the guise of "caring for and protecting" children. I cannot have anyone call on me because of what they "perceive" as abuse or neglect.

I've witnessed more people abuse the system in order to gain custody of a child(ren) and to get revenge on an ex. Many professionals abuse the system. They make false reports and hide behind the "I am a mandated reporter and that is what I am supposed to do." Sure. Many are professional liars and troublemakers who can care less about the children they have reported on. Many are cowards who exercise their power to hurt others. I am not about to have Social Services coming into my home, going through my refrigerator, asking me how much money I make, and the list goes on and on. We do this because mandated reporters make reports based off "their suspicions." They suspect you are not a good parent; therefore, they file a report. Having Social Services involved in your life can be intrusive and stressful. I do not need that kind of stress in my life. I went off into la la land for a brief moment. I have a plan. I am going to taper off and disappear.

From: Larry Pina

To: Lisa Davis

No Subject

January 25, 2018 @ 4:17AM

Heyyyyyyyyyyy Babe, how have you been doing? I miss you soooooooooooooooooooooooooooooooooooooooooooooooooo oooooooooooooooooooooooooooo much. I have been out in the field and yeah, I will be back in the states again. You won't have to miss me anymore. Can I have your home address so I can send you something nice? I am going to send you a picture of me and my guys. They say I am happier after I hear from you.

From: Lisa Davis

To: Larry Pina

No Subject

January 25, 2018 @ 11:30AM

Heck No. You cannot have my address. You have been to Dallas twice and we have not met. You could be the killer or rapist. Besides, I don't know you like that. You must be crazy. I have enjoyed this entertainment and you are giving me plenty of material for a book, but my address. HA! You are mucho loco. I will wait for you to give me roses in person or not at all. How about that?

I knew this meeting was never going to happen, but hey…. this keeps me entertained.

I checked the dating sites occasionally. God made us in HIS image so I won't be too harsh. On the evening of January 26, 2018, I decided to send RoyalKing a flirt. He responded quickly.

RoyalKing: Hello Queen.

LovelyLady: Hello King. How are you?

RoyalKing: I am great. What brings you to this site?

LovelyLady: I am trying to meet a White guy, but Black men are reaching out.

RoyalKing: No need to look for a White man. Your Royal King is here. I am going to have to change your mind about a White man. I would not want to see you with you a White man.

LovelyLady: That is so selfish. Your profile says you are looking for White, Asian, Hispanic & Black women. Y'all love others but only want us to love y'all. Sad but true.

RoyalKing: It's not like that. I have dated different races. Black women are crazy.

LovelyLady: White women, Hispanic women and Asian women must be crazy too. You are still single and looking. If women of other ethnicities are perfect and stable, how come there are so many Black men still looking? Something is not right. Besides, it is not fair to say Black women are crazy. You don't know all Black women. You can reference the ones you have dated as "crazy". I'm positive your actions contributed to their psychosis.

RoyalKing: It's like that, huh? I was married and my ex-wife was possessive and jealous. I'm going to try to date other races and see how that goes.

LovelyLady: Women are women. I watch "Deadly Women" on the ID channel, and it is mainly White women who plan their husband's murders. You go right ahead buddy.

RoyalKing: I would like to get to know you. Is that possible?

LovelyLady: What would you like to know? I would like to know if you have any small children. I cannot date a man with small children. I don't want to be friends with a man who has small children. I have witnessed too many children lie and ruin lives and families. I do not welcome that level of stress.

RoyalKing: I would like to know if I can take you out. My son is 24. A graduate of USC and currently lives in California.

LovelyLady: Awesome. My children are grown too. Hey, when is your born date?

RoyalKing: I'm 50 and my birthdate is September 21st. My real name is Richard Nolan. I live in Dallas, TX. I am from Little Rock, Arkansas. I have five brothers on my mother's side. I have a lot of siblings on my father's side. You know how that goes. I moved here to get away from my ex-wife. She was still trying to control who I dated, and we have been divorced almost three years now.

LovelyLady: LOL. Nice to meet you Richard Nolan. My name is Lisa Davis.

Richard and I chatted before exchanging numbers. Of course, his background check came back clean. After exchanging numbers, I noticed our communication was not consistent. Richard sent cute memes in the morning and at night. We rarely talked. I would call but he would not answer. He called back occasionally. Instantly I knew this was not going anywhere.

Chapter 4

From: Larry Pina

To: Lisa Davis

Hey Babe

February 15, 2018 @ 1:28PM

Heyyy Lisa. How have you been?

Larry

I was not entertaining Larry anymore. That ship has sailed. I am gathering good material for a book. So, I will play along until I get tired. Richard and I texted occasionally but no phone conversation. Around February 2018, Richard sends a good morning text. Richard asked if I wanted to go to the movies and see "Black Panther." He was going to be off on President's Day and so was I. This would be our first meet and greet after communicating for a few weeks. We agreed to meet at the Movie Studio Grille in Arlington, TX. He looked exactly like his profile picture. He smelled good too. I gave him the church hug. I could tell something was off. We made small talk as we entered the theater. Wouldn't you know it? "Black Panther" had sold out. It was the middle of the day. Why aren't people at work? I guess they were off too. I am going to see Black Panther today. I googled movie theaters in Fort Worth. "Black Panther" is showing at Movie Tavern on Hulen. Richard asked if I would purchase two tickets and he would buy the food and drinks. I told him I would meet him there.

He opened the door as we entered the movie theater, but we were careful not to touch each other. We were early so we had a couple of cocktails and made small talk. He was quiet. He said he was nervous. Plus, it takes him awhile to open up. I was not in the mood to engage a grown man, so I began playing on Facebook and so did he. We sat down, ordered food and more drinks. Chadwick Boseman and Michael B. Jordan were enough to take my mind off of him. Richard committed an unforgivable act. He began talking during the movie. If you know me, watching movies is one of my favorite past times. Do not disturb me during this sacred time. Movies are a stress reliever for me. They take me away from all that is wrong in the world. I get to look at the creative work of actors/actresses, directors, producers, stunt men and women. I am in a world filled with action and fantasy for one to two hours. Some people need alcohol, marijuana, pills, sex, shopping, men and women; I need a good movie.

I'm sitting next to a stranger who will not stop talking and I am staring at him trying not to say hush up fool. I decided I did not like him at all at that moment. The movie ended and I jumped up. Richard asked me to wait. "My friend told me to stay until after the credits," he said. I sat back down. Richard began talking about his cars. He has several mustangs. He loves cars. I love classic cars as well. I reluctantly began talking about my love for cars. My favorite car is a 67 Mustang convertible. There was an interesting snippet at the end of "Black Panther". It was glimpse into the next Avenger's movie. Oh, how I love Marvel movies.

I thanked Richard for accompanying me to the movies. He walked me to my car and opened my door. I drove off never looking back knowing that was the last time I would ever lay eyes on Richard Nolan. I smiled. Richard nor I texted one another. A few days later, Richard texted and said he had a nice time. I did not hear from him for a long time after that.

From: Lisa Davis

To: Larry Pina

Greetings

February 21, 2018 @ 9:30AM

Larry, this was fun while it lasted. I am so sorry. I cannot date you. I cannot be a mother to a 3-year-old. I have grown selfish. My children were raised by their father not because I did not love them. I did not have a good support system. I would feel some kind of way raising your child when I did not get the opportunity to spend quality time with my own children. Plus, I am free to get up and go, sleep in or do whatever. I think I have secondary trauma from the way my family rejected my children. I just can't do it. Goodbye and God bless."

I filled Tara in with my latest shenanigans. Tara screamed, "Oh no you did not. Are you serious? I am not being insensitive, but her mother is deceased. You will not have baby mama drama. You can groom her to love you. You love children and they love you. Help me understand your reason for this."

I said matter of factly, "I have grown to be selfish. I do not want the responsibility of being a mother to a 3-year-old. I have seen enough foolishness working for this agency. I am not trying to invite unnecessary drama into my life. I will deal with the external drama as long as God has me here, but y'all are not coming into my home disrupting my life because of someone else's opinions. No thank you." Tara let out a belly wrenching laugh. She was laughing but I was serious. Social Services and the way people operate have frightened me. I knew people were cruel and revengeful. I am on the front lines and this system has messed me up a bit. I am not giving up this portion of my list.

Dear God,

People said do away with the list. I cannot compromise on the height and age of the child. God, I am not trying to beg. Please, no one under 6' and no children under 18 years old. In Jesus name. Amen and Amen.

Two weeks later, Major_One reached out to me. Major_One is 54 and 5'8". A divorced father of two. Catholic. I am retired from the Air Force. I am tired of doing life alone. Women have begun playing games and lying just like men. I would like to meet someone who is honest. I enjoy long drives, hunting, watching movies and cooking.

I frowned upon the height but watching movies and cooking stood out to me. Wait a minute. He probably cooks unseasoned chicken and squash casserole. Yuck.

Major_One: Hi, could it be you?

LovelyLady: Hi. No it is not me. What the hey?

Major_One: I am looking for a friend and maybe it can progress?

LovelyLady: How old are your children?

Major_One: 18 & 22. One is in the Army and the other one is finding himself in California. I am a retired Major. I currently work at Lockheed Martin. I am so tired of being alone. I want someone to go out with occasionally. I want a friend. Currently, it is me and my dog.

LovelyLady: I have never gone out with a White guy. I am a little nervous. I don't think I can handle the discrimination that goes along with interracial dating. I chatted with a White guy who was equally as inconsistent as my brothers. You and your dog, huh? Am I the only person who does not have a pet?

Major_One: My ex-wife is Black. We were married for 24yrs. Both of us were virgins when we got married. While stationed in New York, she met a younger guy and ran off with him. I raised our children alone. I have dated but I have not met another love. A part of me is afraid to try. She was my first and only love.

LovelyLady: Oh, you poor thing. Bless your little heart. That fear probably prohibits you from having stable relationships.

I do not like him as a date, but I can identify with him as a service member. I can identify with his hurt. He is too short so I know this will not be a relationship. His real name was Stanley Michaels. Of course, he asked me out and I accepted. Mind you, his profile said he was 5'8". I am 5'9". I was hesitant but I am going to try something new. As a matter of fact, I decided to watch "Something New" starring Sanaa Lathan and Simon Baker for a little encouragement. I am careful not to dress sexy when I meet strangers. I decided to wear flat shoes because he is an inch shorter than me. Again, I found myself at The Movie Tavern on Hulen. I pulled into the parking lot and let Stanley know I was there. Unbeknownst to either of us, we were parked right next to each other.

Oh dear, I am nervous. He passed his background check, but I binged watched the ID channel last night and every episode the White man was a rapist or the killer. I don't know if I was nervous because he was White or short. As he exited his car, my stomach dropped. He was not 5'8". He was freaking 5'7". I'm a little peeved at that point. I had to talk myself down. Do not call this man a liar. Do not call this man a liar. Smile Lisa. You are here now. I extended my hand and greeted him kindly. We entered the movie theater amidst stares from White women and Black men. I can be kind of gangsterish. I stared back. Stanley paid for the movie. We opted to see Jumanji starring Dwayne "The Rock" Johnson, Kevin Hart and Jack Black. He offered to buy me food, but I had lost my appetite. His height messed me up.

I was disturbed because he was two inches shorter than me. I was thinking you lying wonder. I reluctantly accepted to meet you for a date because you are one inch shorter than me. Noooooooooo, you are two inches shorter than me. I am giving him the side eye. This one began talking and he talked nonstop during the movie. Now, I am questioning whether or not I really want to date. These men are aggravating creatures whether Black or White. He kept asking if I wanted anything. I said, "Nope. My stomach feels weird." This was not a lie. My stomach was filled with disappointment. I just want to go home. “I am going home after this. I just want to lie down.”

“I thought you wanted to go out to eat after the movies,” he said.

“Nah. I just want to go home.”

The movie ended. We watched the outtakes and credits. We went to our perspective cars. He turned to me and said, “You don’t like me, do you?”

I said, “No”. I drove off never looking back.

I chatted with several guys from February to April 2018. I did not meet anyone else after Stanley. I did not want to meet anyone. I chatted for pure entertainment and material for a book. This will make a great read. I wonder if other women are going through this. Someone will be able to identify with these experiences. WBS: there is no difference between Black men or White men. If he lied about his height, what else is he going to lie about?

Chapter 5

In April, my best friend Tina and I flew to California. That was a fun trip. I loved Malibu beach and The Hollywood Walk of Fame. I loved the beach. The waves, the serenity, the surfing and parasailing and those big, beautiful mountains made me want to climb them. Not really. I just like looking at God's creation. Only God can create that kind of beautimous. Beautimous is a word I like to use to describe gorgeousness. I can care less about the growing trend of grammar Nazis. Mountains are beautimous and so is water. I was able to take a picture of Keanu Reeves star on the strip. I looked for Denzel's star but did not find him. I was bummed about that but maybe next time. I love California and would move there but it is too expensive for my budget.

We drove back which gave us time to laugh and reminiscence. We laughed at our failed relationships. We laughed and laughed some more. California traffic is a beast. We pulled over and went to Walmart in order to kill some time. We spent at least two hours if not longer in Walmart hoping traffic would be lighter. Absolutely not. Traffic was bad. Traffic finally lifted as we drove through Coachella. We drove through Coachella not realizing Beyonce was the headliner. Yesssss Queen B. I love me some Beyonce. We drove through more mountains. I did not have a care in the world. I was doing some of my favorite things with one of my favorite people. We were driving, listening to music and site seeing. This is called living.

KingTut reached out to me. Another Black guy on InterracialDating.com.

KingTut: I am 52. 6' tall and have a few extra pounds. I am divorced with six children. All of them are grown and out on their own. I want to date but have not found anyone I really like. Plus, I have to let women know I have been to federal prison. I used to sell drugs. I served my time. I have a legal job. I am on parole and will complete it in three months. We don't have to get serious. I just want to hang out, go to the movies or do whatever she likes to do.

LovelyLady: Thanks for your transparency. A former drug dealer. Oh, I have a lot of questions. How old were you when you begin selling drugs? How long were you in prison? How did you get caught? Oh dear. Were you as huge as Frank Lucas? Denzel played him in American Gangster. Umph, Umph, Umph. Congratulations on your legal job. Is it legal until you get off parole? Black man stop giving these White folks your freedom. I know fast money is appealing. However, this system and world is built for the success of the Wypipo. White folks own the planes, trains and boats. They transport the drugs to America. They allow you Negroes to make a little change. Once you get too big. They lock your assets up. You lose regardless. More children without a father. The cycle continues. SMH! I am not being critical. I am tired of people who look like me doing illegal crap and getting locked up for it. Losing our men to the penal system is affecting all of us.

I told Tina I don't have to run a background check on him. He told the truth. I would run a background check just to make sure he is not the killer. We laughed.

Tina said, "You and these killers. Stop watching that damn ID channel."

I laughed and said, "No ma'am. There are more killers out there than I thought." I continued. "Did you know some people have married in order to get additional insurance policies and then killed their spouses or have them murdered? I recommend that everyone watches the ID Channel in order to learn a thing or two. Some people are born killers, and some pick up that evil spirit along the way. I do not want to sleep with one eye open. I already have trouble sleeping. Did you see that movie "Sleeping with The Enemy" starring Julia Roberts? That movie was based off someone else's experience. We laughed but I was serious.

This guy's real name was Wayne Michaels. That made me smile because my brother's name is Michael DeWayne…..imagine that. We chatted for a bit and eventually changed numbers. He called me every day and sometimes several times per day. After two weeks, he invited me to dinner. I choose my favorite restaurant which is Chili's. Wayne was an attractive guy. He was mild mannered and respectful.

He grew up in Waco, TX. He began selling drugs as a teenager. He did not have to sell drugs because his parents taught them their worth. He and his siblings attended college and were raised in church. Wayne explained, "My parents were married till death did them part. My father was a proud man. He told us we could be anything we wanted to be. He encouraged us to go to college. That level of pride he instilled in me made me cocky. I was a high school football star. I could have any girl I wanted. That fueled my ego," Wayne continued. "I noticed the neighborhood drug dealers driving cars I wanted to drive. So, I connected with them, and the rest is history."

"How did you get caught?" I asked.

"My wife was threatened by the feds. She told them everything. I cannot forgive her for that."

"Is she the mother of your children?"

"Yes," he answered.

"Well, you have to forgive her. You will probably go back to her. You are just bitter right now."

"I will never go back to her. She turned me in to the feds and she spent all of my money."

I smiled. I could tell by the passion in his voice that he was going back to her eventually. We sat there for four hours talking about nothing and talking about everything. He promised that he was respectful. He was not going to pressure me for sex. He simply wanted a friend and for that I was grateful. Wayne asked if we could meet for dinner the following weekend to which I agreed. On Sunday, April 15th, we met at Movie Studio Grille in Arlington. We went to see "The Quiet Place" starring John Krasinski and Emily Blunt. Wayne paid for the movie and the food. He was quiet throughout the movie. I appreciated his quietness, and I enjoyed the movie. There was no attraction.

Wayne called me every day. He gave me a play by play of his morning, noon and night. He worked 3-11pm. He called me on his lunch break. He would text me to let me know he made it home. I would see the text when I woke up the next morning. At least he is consistent, but there is that gnawing feeling he is going back to his ex-wife. Unforgiveness and bitterness can blind us. He was a man who was scorned. In the meantime, I am grateful for his friendship.

Chapter 6

On April 19, 2018, I received news that felt like my heart had been ripped out of my chest. My cousin called to tell me that my baby brother was dead. My head begin to spin. I let out a scream so loud and deafening. I did not recognize my own voice. This can't be true. This is not true. I continued to get dressed because I had to conduct a family assessment. I just talked to Big Mike. I told him I was coming to visit in June. My cousin said she is almost positive it is Big Mike. Since she is not sure, there is a possibility this is not happening. She said she will call me back shortly.

I sat on the sofa and waited for confirmation. I looked at my phone and saw the text. At that same moment, my aunt was calling, and I heard the tears in her voice. My entire body began to shake. My mother and my brother are gone. I could not breathe. I felt like someone was smothering me. She asked if someone was here with me. I screamed, "NO! I am always freaking alone."

"Where are your sons? Someone needs to be there with you?" She stated matter-of-factly. I could not talk nor breathe. She kept saying Lisa. Lisa. Lisa. Lisa. "Lord have mercy. She does not have anyone with her. Lord help her."

I finally caught my breath. Aunt Sugar asked, "What are you doing?" "I am going to get dressed. I have to meet with a family."

"Lisa, that job can wait. You need to take care of you right now."

I snapped, "I can't be still. I need to do something. If I sit here, I feel like I might break."

"Call me when you get in, so I will know you are safe. Love you." Okay Bye."

I called my supervisor to let her know my brother passed and I am overwhelmed. She told me to stay home, and she will find someone to cover for me. I told her I cannot sit still. I have to move. I drove to the office and put on a brave face. As soon as I pulled into the parking lot, my supervisor and a coworker were walking outside. My supervisor said she was not going to say anything. She just wanted to give me a hug. I lost it. I needed a hug. I entered the office and gathered all of the information I needed for my family assessment. While driving, my phone was ringing off the hook. None of the numbers were recognizable but the area code was. 662 and 601 are Mississippi area codes. I answered a few calls. A few of my classmates were offering their condolences.

I wondered they'd gotten my number. One of my friends from the first grade had shared my loss with the class of 1985 and encouraged them to call me. I arrived at the family's home around 5:45pm. I sat and listened to an ungrateful teen complain about her home life while surrounded by her parents, aunt, brother and sister. Inside I am hurting. Through that hurt, I told the ungrateful teenager that her parents love her enough to have boundaries. Having a curfew and obeying house rules do not equate to abuse. I told her that it appears as though she has a loving family. I shared that my mother and brother are deceased. I would trade places with her today if I could. She cried and apologized to her parents for lying. Social services have made it easy for children to lie on their parents. Every child is not being abused or neglected. At any rate, I completed my assessment and headed back home around 7:30pm. A few more classmates called me. I asked my friend to take down the post. Unfortunately, the class of 1985 has never been close. I don't think we dislike each other. People like and support whomever they deem worthy. The gesture was kind, but I only wanted to hear from people who actually loved me and vice versa.

I shared the news of my brother's passing with Wayne. He offered his condolences. I told him I will be heading to the Mississippi Delta. Wayne said, "I am sorry I cannot go with you.

I cannot travel while on parole. Can you meet me somewhere so I can give you some gas money? It won't help ease the pain, but it will help with expenses." Wayne gave me $300.00. He promised to check on me every day for support. He kept his promise.

This was going to be a long drive. I hopped in my car and traveled along 20 east. I tried not to think about my brother or loss of life. I listened to music and sang along. My phone rang often. Family wanted to know if I had left yet, friends and coworkers offering moral support. I eased on down the road. Much to my surprise, Richard Nolan called. "Hey stranger" said the voice coming through the Bluetooth.

"Hey yourself."

"How have you been?"

"I can't complain."

"What are you up to?"

"I'm headed to Mississippi. My brother passed away and we are having his funeral on Sunday."

"I am so sorry for your loss. I have been traveling back and forth to Arkansas because my mother has been ill. I wish I could be there for you. You and your family are in my prayers. Let me know if you need anything."

I thanked him for calling but did not feel like being bothered.

The signs read right lane closed ahead. Oh brother. Whoever has the contract to repair highways will never lose a job. They have been working on this stretch of highway for at least five years. While sitting and barely moving, my aunt called. She asked how close I was to making it. "I am six hours away. I'm sitting in traffic, and it is not really moving."

"We went to the funeral home to view the body. The funeral home director told us we did not want to see him. My sister viewed the body and said it was him. The funeral will have to be a closed casket because the blood rushed to his head, and he is dark and swollen. I did not want to see him like that, and I don't think you should see him like that."

I cried silently because she would not understand. I love my family, but they have no tact. Here I am driving to bury my brother. The only sibling, I had on my mother's side. My baby brother and you tell me there will be a closed casket because he is unrecognizable.

My head began to throb. I had to talk myself down. I cannot lose control because I am driving. *Please don't break Lisa. Please don't break.* My aunt is asking if I am okay. I want to scream NOOOO I am not okay. The pain and insensitivity are too much. God, I am hurting right now. How insensitive to hear this news? She could not have waited until I arrived. This isn't happening again. A few years earlier, my mother passed. I was living in Gulfport, MS during this time. I was at work when my cousin called and told me the doctor said I needed to get to the hospice. My mother had cancer. She was diagnosed with cancer in January, and it was now July. I spent as much time with her as I could. I drove back and forth to Jackson, MS in order to spend time, mend fences and pray with her. She had been moved from the hospital to hospice one month earlier.

It didn't take a rocket science to know what was about to happen. My cousin told me the doctor wanted me there before she took her last breath. I am hopeful but uncertain. I am nervous and anxious. *Hang on Bernice. I am on my way.* I had gone to visit her the previous Saturday. Today is Wednesday. The drive from Gulfport to Jackson, MS is almost three hours. I was careful not to speed. I did not want to hurt myself or anyone else. I was an hour out when I called, and my cousin said she was hanging in there. He told me to take my time and get there safely. Forty-five minutes later, another relative called and is screaming through the phone, "She is gone Lisa. Your mother is gone." Tears swelled in my eyes. I knew this was going to happen. Not now. She was supposed to wait. I am on my way. My eyes were filled with tears and the highway was no longer visible. I don't remember how I ended up on side of the highway. I sat on the side of highway 49 South sobbing uncontrollably.

I called my friend Tiffany who directed me to stay right there, and she offered to come and get me. I told her I was halfway there. I gathered myself before I continued my drive. How silly can my family be? Why would you do that? Why would you tell me that my mother passed away? You knew I was driving alone. My heart was heavy. I arrived at hospice just in time to close my mother's eyes and kiss her on the cheek. I wanted to lash out and tell my family how stupid they were. I was angry and sad. I was mad and wanted to hurt someone because I was hurting. I opted to go to the chapel instead.

Fade to the future, I'm driving down the highway to bury yet another loved one only to hear news that would punch me in the gut. I don't know if there is a such thing as funeral etiquette, but my family needs a class. They know how to pour salt on an open wound. Geesh people. I know I am a prayer warrior, but I am also human. I bleed and hurt too. I have to carry all of my hurt alone which makes it difficult. After burying my mother, I had to go back to Gulfport alone. There was no one to comfort me. After I bury my brother, I will have to go back to Fort Worth alone. God, I trust you but this hurts.

I checked into the Days Inn motel in Indianola, MS. I did not want to be around anyone. I was angry. I was angry because I will not get the closure , I need. I will not be able to see my brother's beautiful face one last time. I just wanted to sulk in silence. I did just that. As promised, Wayne checked to see if I had arrived. I did not feel like talking to anyone. I responded a simple yes via text. The funeral precession was really small. The majority of our intimate family members have passed away. The hearse and the limo woke me up out of my fantasy. This is real. I'm about to bury my baby brother. This is my brother who never bothered a soul. He was quiet and mild mannered. He was the opposite of me. I was wild and crazy. I smiled in spite of. We lined up in front of the church. As I entered the church, I saw three of my childhood friends. They were there when my mother died, and they are here now. I smiled and they smiled back. I looked ahead at the gold casket with the beautiful flower draped across it. I looked at his picture standing tall on an easel. Not my Michael. I did not think I was going to cry. I had cried enough over the past week. I did not think I had any more tears. Boy was I wrong. This is final. This is the same place we funeralized my mother, one of my favorite cousins, one of my favorite aunts and now my baby brother.

God, I know you are listening. I don't mean to be selfish, but I would like it if you will allow me and my other family members to live fifty more years. As the preacher preached and the psalmist sang, I wept, and I wept. This was it. The funeral was over. They rolled the casket out and we followed behind it. Everyone had someone to hold their hands except me. I walked out of the church alone, without comfort and no one noticed. I was shaking. I almost fell because my legs felt like jell-o. Again, no one noticed. I was too emotional to ask for help. No one noticed me either. At that moment, I felt unloved and unnoticed. At that moment, I realized how alone I was and how alone I have always been. Death was hard, but this felt like hell.

We drove to the cemetery. My maternal grandparents who raised me are out there. My favorite cousin Annie Marie is out there. One of my favorite aunts, Baboo is out there. My mother, Bernice is out there and now my baby brother will join them. I did not walk through the cemetery because I did not want to see their graves. I am not the type who visits graves. The Bible says the dead do not know what we are doing. That is why I try to celebrate family members while they are alive.

My wonderful family and their lack of compassion is never ending. Over and over different relatives said, "Umph, Umph, Umph. Your mother is gone. Your brother is gone. Now it's just you. You don't have nobody. Well, you have us." I stood there silent. In my mind I had punched her in the face a few times. I never responded. She hugged me but I did not hug her back. I looked up to heaven and asked, "Am I on candid camera?" I am already feeling alone, and you had to point that out to me.

No funeral is without its share of drama. There were lies upon more lies. False accusations and people who wanted to take all of the credit for doing this or that. I smiled inwardly. I was trying to process whether or not to throw blows and give the people something to talk about or take the high road. As always, I choose the latter. Sometimes the best response is no response. The only voice I put on family is power of prayer. I did not want to stick around.

On Monday, I headed back to Fort Worth. I was numb. I was absolutely numb. Wayne called to see how I was doing. I was not ready to talk to anyone. I needed to focus on the highway. If I started talking, I was going to start crying. I did not want to have an accident and myself or someone else. Over and over, I kept saying, "Psalm 118:17 I will not die but live and declare the works of the Lord." I was determined more than ever to enjoy my life. I felt guilty making plans to enjoy life, but I was not ready to die. We only get one shot, and I am going to make the best of it. Before my mother passed, she made me promise that I would not give up on living or love. She made me promise that I would get married and live a long happy life. She did not want me to live alone or die alone like she did. I promised her that I would get married and enjoy life. I do not have to get married in order to enjoy life, but I want to enjoy life. My mother died at the age of 57 and Michael has died at the age of 46. Both were young. In my defense, I did get married but we know how that turned out. On a brighter note, I have not given up on love.

I was due to go back to work on Wednesday. I called out the rest of the week. I needed to unwind and process my emotions. A job will work the hell out of you but only gives you three days to grieve your loved ones. Three days is not enough time to process grief.

Chapter 7

From: Larry Pina

To: Lisa Davis

Hi

April 26, 2018 @ 7:46AM

How are you doing Lisa? How is life treating you? Are you married now?

From: Lisa DavisTo: Larry Pina

April 26, 2018 @ 8:11PM

LOL. No. I am not married. I am still waiting on the one God has ordained for me.

A white guy who resembled Edward Norton reached out to me. BaldEagle01 response: Hi. I am not into playing games. I have my MBA. I have a lucrative career. I own a home and drive a BMW. I do not have any children, nor do I want any. I am married and divorced. I want someone who is emotionally and financially stable. I am not going to do all of the providing. I expect a woman to be self-sufficient. I only date Black women. It is not a thing. It is a preference. I found your picture to be absolutely gorgeous. I would love to chat with you and take you out if possible. I do have a German Sheppard.

As I read his profile, I could see the arrogance oozing off the screen. I am not going out with him because he has a dog. I am going to respond just because.

LovelyLady: How are you? You sound accomplished. I don't know if I am interested in serious dating. We can chat.

I did not hear from BaldEagle01 nor did I reach out to him. I forgot about him until I received an alert.

BaldEagle01: I have not heard from you.

LovelyLady: I have not heard from you either.

BaldEagle01: You probably lack the intelligence to have a decent conversation.

LovelyLady: Whoa cowboy! Anger issues??

BaldEagle01: I see I am right by your reply. I do not deal with stupid people. I cannot stand stupid people. You stupid bitch. That is probably why you don't have anyone.

I laughed so hard. I did not have to delete his profile. He deleted me. That was the funniest and most weird experience. He was probably the killer. I laughed again. I chatted with men from Virginia, South Carolina, Tennessee, and Florida. There were naked men, men without shirts, men in robes, ministers, deacons, teachers, doctors, nurses, and firemen. You name it and they were online in search of love, lust, affairs, fantasies, companionship, casual dating, marriage and sex. One would have to navigate through profiles and trust your inner self on who and when you wanted to meet a person.

Wayne and I chatted a few more times after that. He invited me out to dinner for Mother's Day, but I knew that was not going to happen. I get this sensation in the pit of my stomach when something is not right. There is a stirring that takes place. I can't describe but it is almost like an internal warning system. The week before Mother's Day, I had attended a prophetic conference in Arlington, TX. Dr. Uyi Abraham prayed for single women. His prayer was simple yet effective. He prayed that any man not meant for us to be loosed now and not waste our time. He prayed for godly husbands to be released not boyfriends and players.

On the evening of May 13, 2018, Wayne called and said, "I am so sorry for leading you on. My ex-wife has been reaching out to me and she told me she was sorry. I am going to give her another chance. Please don't be mad. You are too nice, and I needed to let you know."

I smiled. "Wayne, I told you that you were going back to her. No worries. Hey, God bless you and your family. I appreciate your support. You are a nice guy and there are no hard feelings." I patted myself on the back. Dang I'm good. Stevie Wonder could have seen that one coming. On that note, I went to sleep.

Chapter 8

I have been at this dating thing since October 2017. It is May 2018 and I'm batting a zero. I deleted the interracial dating site because I realized Fitz was a fantasy and I am not Olivia Pope. I decided to leave my profile up on the free dating site. In the meantime, I engaged in grief counseling. I am functioning but broken. My nights and days were filled with thoughts of my brother. He was never married and did not have any children. All I have are memories. I was guilty because I told him I was coming to visit in June. Well, it is almost June, and I won't see him. I felt different. I felt like a piece of me had died.

Do not fall into a depression Lisa. Press. Do the work to get healed. Death leaves an open wound that heals slowly. It does not get easier, but it does get better. Press. You cannot bring him back. You can die slowly. Live Lisa. Press. I had to encourage myself because there was no one else to do it. I realized that when you lose a loved one people call and offer emotional support. After the burial, the phone calls stop. In my opinion, support is needed after the burial because that is when the healing begins. I don't have a good support system. Heck, I am the support system for many. Most of the people around me are self-centered. They are a priority to themselves, and I have contributed to it by making them a priority over me. No longer will my family and friends needs come before my own. I'm going to start taking care of my needs first. I am finally putting me first and I won't feel guilty about it.

In addition to movies, I love to read. I am going to find more things to do in order to help relieve stress. Dating is one of those things I am going to do. I am determined to date because I need someone to take my mind off of my brother and the loneliness I am feeling. I have been single more than I have been married or in any relationship. I have been alone but now I am lonely. I am hurting. Big Mike's death has shaken me. I purchased books on overcoming grief. I purchased books to help me understand why I do the things I do. I wanted to understand my love language.

My favorite reads are "Why You Do The Things You Do?" by Dr. Tim Clinton and Dr. Gary Sibcy, and The "5 Love Languages" by Gary Chapman. "Why You Do The Things You Do?" took me on a journey that began with my childhood. The answer to the way many of us do relationships can be found based off our childhood experiences.

"Why do we do the things we do? All of us cause pain in relationships as well as experience it-and we can't help ourselves. And we keep going back for more! The persistent human cry is for someone to love us. Our need for relationship is even more powerful than our need for food" (Dr. Clinton & Dr. Gary Sibcy pg. 8 & 9). This book is informative, enlightening and transformative. This is good. I am learning a lot and willing to apply lessons learned. The "Five Love Languages" are words of affirmation, gifts, acts of service, quality time, and physical touch. I have realized that I value words of affirmation. A simple thank you, thinking of you or missing you will go a long way with me. Quality time comes in a close second. I like talking and sharing intimate thoughts. I would love someone to play a game of UNO, take a long drive or go walking with me. Physical touch is number three, followed by acts of service and gifts.

I prefer a man not buy me gifts because I am picky. Ray is the only man who has ever bought me decent gifts. Most of the time I am displeased with the gift's men buy. I encourage men to buy me purses or perfume. I figure he won't be able to screw that up.

I had forgotten about my profile on Plenty of Fish. Multiple alerts were notifying me that I had a lot of activity. Many of the guys lived too far. I do not feel like driving to and from in order to meet anyone. Men reached out to me from Frisco, Plano, Houston, Waco, Amarillo, Irving, Abilene, McKinney and the list goes on. Are there any single men in Fort Worth?

On May 21, 2018, I received an alert from AToughOne. He sent me a flirt. I zoomed in on his profile picture. He was posing in a t-shirt and flexing a muscle. His eyes looked funny. Not in an unattractive way but in a humorous way. He looked like a funny guy. One who would make me laugh. I clicked on his profile.

His profile reads, AToughOne is a 53 single man who lives in Fort Worth. 6'0, Christian (other), bachelor's degree. I don't have any children. I am looking for a serious relationship. I am tired of playing games. I work out and take good care of my physical health. I want to meet someone who is funny, smart and attractive. I'm a small business owner.

LovelyLady: Hi.

AToughOne: I am glad you responded. It is some crazy stuff going on in these chat rooms. I just want to meet a good woman. I am a good man and want someone to compliment my life.

He immediately sent his name and phone number. His name is William Antoine Smith. I called and we talked for hours. We shared our ups and downs in dating. He has never been married. I have been married and divorced twice. He told me he was with his last girlfriend for 5 years. They broke up because she cheated on him. Although, I'm positive he cheated first. According to William, they were engaged but she broke up with him and married someone else one month later. I told him that she probably married someone because he had been stringing her along for five years. That should have been a red flag.

He said, "My ex was a narcissist. I did not know what a narcissist was until another woman I dated told me. I remember looking through her cabinets and seeing psychotropic medication."

"Medication does not help narcissists," I added.

He said, "I believe she had depression and Bipolar."

"You knew that within the first year of dating her and yet you stayed for five years."

"Well, I am the type that when I am with a woman, I am with her. Men get comfortable. We do not like to start over."

Before getting off the phone, he invited me to meet him the next day for dinner at Boomer Jack's downtown Fort Worth. I don't want to meet the next day. I asked him his born date which is August 21st. While we were talking, I conducted a background check. He had a misdemeanor in 2004 and no other charges. We agreed to meet at Montgomery Plaza at 8pm on Thursday, May 24th.

I let my coworker and cousin know I was going to meet William Smith at BoomerJacks. I sent my coworker a picture that I had screenshot from the dating site. She could not run point because she had to work. Monica gave me strict instructions to take a picture of his car and the license plate. Again, I am careful not to dress sexy when meeting a stranger. I wore a lavender and black cardigan, a lavender tank, jeans and lavender sandals. I accessorized with silver jewelry. I drove around and could not locate Boomer Jack's. I called William and he asked which restaurant was in front of me because he would come and get me. It was Pei Wei's Chinese restaurant. He directed me to walk down to the corner, take a left and Boomer Jack's would be to my right. He explained he was heading back that way. I noticed an attractive man walking towards me in a grey t-shirt and black athletic pants. He was approximately 6'. We hugged and he screamed with excitement.

He said, "Oh shucks, you are gorgeous. I am pleased."

He held the door open and was extremely attentive. He was nice to the hostess as he requested a table for two. The hostess escorted us to a table in an inconvenient section. He asked if I was satisfied with the table, but I was not. There was an open booth. He escorted me to the booth. He waited for me to sit before he sat down.

He ordered beer after beer. I smiled because I could tell he had been drinking prior to meeting me. Either he is nervous, or he likes to drink. He is a talker. He talked to the waitress and the people at the next table. He talked about wanting a healthy relationship with a woman who is faithful. I listened and observed. He continuously talked about his ex. All I could do was smile. Men use the "she cheated on me as a way to reel a woman in." It makes him appear to be a good man. He garners your pity. It is game ladies. You can proceed but know that it is manipulation. I did not believe him, nor did I respond.

We talked for hours. "Why is a tall and beautiful woman like you single?"

"I really can't answer that. I have noticed every man I have met with the exception of Ray has been attached to his ex-wife or girlfriend. It is as if the men can't let go of the past. Plus, I am nice, and men tend to take advantage of me or shall I say take me for granted."

"I want a good woman. I am not going to take advantage of a woman who is good to me. I'm not attached to my ex. I would not piss on her if she was on fire."

I did not believe him. This has been a pattern for me. I don't understand why people won't go back to people who broke them. Those people have their hearts, minds and souls. I drifted off and was deep in my own thoughts for a minute. I'm discerning a prideful spirit. He was funny. We laughed and laughed some more. At that moment, I realized I needed to laugh. I ordered catfish, fries and a margarita. I ate it all. I told William I am not one of those salad eating chicks. I ate everything on my plate. We had a good time. We parted ways. He asked me to call him when I make it home. I decided I would not call him. I figured he would call me if he was interested.

I arrived home around 10:30pm. William called to see if I had arrived home.

"Hi, I was checking to see if you made it home."

"I am home." "What are you doing?" He asked.

"I am getting ready for bed." I responded.

"I really enjoyed you tonight. Man, it felt good going out and having a good time."

I said, "Yes that was nice."

"I have not been sleeping good since my favorite uncle died."

"Me either. Sorry for your loss. My brother passed in April." I noticed William never said thanks or sorry for your loss. I'm thinking not another self-absorbed man God have mercy.

"Do you go to church?" I asked.

"No. Not anymore. These preachers are only after money" he said.

I sat in silence as he ranted. "I believe in God and Jesus. I believe America is going to be judged. Israel will be the last nation standing. We are going back to Israel because we descended from Israel. If you don't believe me do your research. I began to giggle. *Yep. This dude is wasted. I could hear it in his voice.* At first I couldn't remember what sparked this portion of the conversation. Now I remember. I asked if he would go to church with me if we build a friendship. William said, "As long as your pastor is not a woman. I am not going to listen to a woman. The bible says a woman is not supposed to teach a man. The church is out of order. A man is the head of a woman."

I remained silent because I have learned not to argue with fools. There isn't anything I can do or say that was going to change his mind. We said good night.

I woke up to a good morning beautiful text. That was nice and thoughtful. Here we go again. Dating is a cycle of disappointments. We meet, we show interest, we text, and we talk but it tapers off and the process starts all over again. I went to the office and Tara could not wait to hear how the date went.

She burst into my office with a big smile. “How did it go?”

My affect was flat. “It went pretty good. I don’t know about him. He is nice but it something about him. He went on and on about his ex-girlfriend. Plus, he went on and on about his disapproval of women ministers. He is religious and prideful.”

Tara said, “Give him a chance. That is just a difference in opinion. Your brother just passed, and you need someone to hang out with. Go to dinner and have fun.” That dang Tara always sees the upside of things.

I went through a checklist of things. He is funny and entertaining. He is good for a laugh. He texted and called all day on Friday. Later that night, I received another blow. My cousin James had been shot and killed. My mind was racing. I just saw James at Michael’s funeral. No. This can’t be happening. Not again God. It is too soon. God, I asked you not to allow my family to feel this type of pain for years to come. Again, I could not breathe. I don’t understand. It is not my place to understand. All James does is smile. Who would want to hurt him? My cousin reached out to me and said they were going to have a balloon release in honor of James. They are going to release yellow balloons because he was always happy. Due to my work schedule, I kind of knew I would not be able to make the funeral. I had to make it to the balloon release because all of them were with me when I buried my brother.

My phone lit up and it was William. “Hello. Sir. How are you?”

“I’m good. Wondering when I would see you again?”

“Well, I am going out of town this weekend. My cousin was shot and killed.”

"Oh wow. When are you leaving? Are you going to Mississippi?"

"I'm leaving now, and I am heading to Jackson, MS."

"Who is going with you?"

"I'm going alone."

"I will check on you and make sure you get there. If I had known you long enough, I could have gone with you." He would have gone with me but did not offer to drive me.

"Chat with you later," I said.

Here I am driving 20 East again. God, make it stop. I turn on Sirius XM and listen to Todd Delaney's "Your Great Name". I began singing along and I felt alive. I felt guilty for being alive. I felt the joy of being alive. In honor of Big Mike, Lame James and all those who proceeded them in death, I want to live. Maybe I will enjoy going out on dates with William. He doesn't seem like the serious type. I need to have some fun right now.

William called several times throughout the day. That was really nice. It felt good having someone to check on me as I drove to Jackson. I noticed right away that he was rude. He would say hold on but never clicked back over to me. I would hang up. He would call twenty or thirty minutes later to say that he is a small business owner and has to take calls. He lacked common courtesy. This happened several times while I was driving. I decided I would not answer if he called back.

I drove straight to E & L's BBQ on Bailey Avenue in Jackson, MS. I ordered rib tips and hot links with sauce on fries. I drove to the Super 8 Motel in Pearl, MS. I unloaded the car and smashed my food. William called off and on throughout the evening and in the wee hours of the morning. He couldn't sleep and neither could I. We talked and talked some more. He was silly and fun to talk to.

Of course, I continued checking the dating site because I do not want to settle for the first guy who shows interest. I wanted to talk to at least five different guys because I needed to see how the conversation goes and to see who is really interested. My mentor taught me the term circular dating. Circular dating is when you date multiple guys. You don't have to sleep with them. The goal is not to get serious with one guy too soon. There is a lot of uncertainty in modern day dating. One guy will get you emotionally invested, and he will disappear. I could be wrong, but William seems to be one of those guys who is going to disappear. I give it less than six months. He is too silly.

Off and on, different guys reached out to me. However, William was the only one who consistently called and texted. Everyone else wanted sex. No first date. No getting to know me, my wants/needs, dreams or goals…only sex. Getting to know someone sucks. It is exhausting.

On Saturday morning, I woke up hungry as usual. I found the nearest Krystal on Highway 80. I don't know why but food excites me. I ordered a number one which is four Krystal burgers with no cheese, fries and a medium coke. I asked for extra ketchup and mustard. I can't wait to get back to the hotel and smash these burgers.

I entered the hotel, sat crossed legged on the bed, prepped my food with the necessary condiments and the burgers are now history. My cousin Tonya called to see what time I was heading to her mother's house. Tonya is my second cousin. Her mother, Dorothea is my first cousin. Dorothea and I were raised more like sisters. That is how it was back then. Your cousins became your sisters and brothers. I headed to Jackson around 1pm. William texted and asked if I would send him a picture. I requested one in return. He was easy on the eyes.

I arrived at Dorothea's apartment around 1:15p or so. I'm happy to see my family but also sad due to the occasion. This is surreal. More and more family started to drop by. My cousin Main brought packs of chicken, smoked sausage, hot dogs and hamburgers. Cousin Catrina and her best friend made the macaroni & cheese. Someone else made baked beans and potato salad. It is amazing how food brings us comfort during a time of loss. We released yellow balloons in memory of James. The entire day was beautiful. The weather, food and family were as close to perfect as can be.

I said my goodbyes and went back to the hotel. I showered and dressed for bed. I received an alert.

Herman007: Hey, pretty lady.

LovelyLady: Hi.

Herman007: What brings you to this dating site?

LadyLove: Same as you I suppose.

Herman007: I am looking to date a woman who is faithful. I am tired of meeting women who sleep around.

LadyLove: Let me guess. Your ex cheated on you (rolls eyes).

Herman007: Yes. She cheated on me. I travel a lot and she was doing her thang. I built her up She had bad credit. I paid off bills, co-signed for her car and helped her get on her feet. She repays me by cheating.

LadyLove: Lately, every man I talk to has a “cheating” ex-wife, girlfriend or fiancé. One thing I know is, a man cannot take what he dishes out. I’m starting to believe men like whorish women just as much as women like whorish men. Men chase those women just like women chase those men. Something is not right with this picture.

Herman007: What is your story?

LovelyLady: Plain and simple. I keep meeting men who are hung up on their exes. I have not met a man with a different story. Every man I meet sounds exactly the same, “I paid all of the bills. I put her through college. I loved her. I was faithful to her. I was there for her.” By the time I meet one of you jokers, I can’t even get a dinner date. Sad but true. I know most of you are lying. You are trying to make yourself look chivalrous, but I cannot believe a woman would mess up a relationship whereas a man is paying her bills etc. At any rate, every man I have met says the same thing. When it comes to me, I buy my own everything.

Herman007: Honestly, I am not doing all of that for another woman. I will not allow a woman to use me again. I am not paying for trips or anything anymore.

LovelyLady: You are wounded. You have allowed an experience to stop you from being who you are. Every woman is not a whore or user. But hey, you like what you like. I think I just want someone to hang out with occasionally. The more I talk to men the more nervous I am becoming. All of you are over 50 but I do not like what I am hearing.

Herman007: I am a Christian man. I know that is what you are looking for. I attend the Potter's House in Dallas. In my spare time, I like to go out with my friends. We are loud. We like to play cards and laugh. We have a few drinks. We are a group of professional man who love to have fun. I absolutely will not be paying bills for anyone else.

LovelyLady: Awe. That is nice. Bless your heart.

There is no point in asking his real name or conducting a background check. I am not feeling this at all. Plus, I do not like his eyes. Herman sent his phone number and requested a call. I told him I would call him tomorrow.

I went to sleep around 4:30am. I was awakened by the maid bursting into the room. She'd startled me. I jumped up and was in fight mode. I was disoriented. I looked at the clock and it was 9 freaking 30 in the morning. Check out was at noon. I was irritated.

"Leave, please," I said calmly.

“I’m sorry miss,” the maid said as she was backing out of the room. I started fussing to the air. She is sorry. Sorry heifer. Trying to rush guests out of the hotel. I should have kicked her. I jumped back under the covers and tried to go back to sleep. I tossed and turned. Dang it man. I can’t sleep. It was 10:00 am. I might as well get up, get dressed and hit the road. I’m not leaving Pearl, MS without a Krystal burger. That put a smile on my face.

I jump into that Nissan Altima and 20 West here I come. On the road again. I will be home in approximately seven hours or less. It is Memorial Day weekend. I get to relax on Monday. I stopped in Monroe, LA in order to see Bonnie and Janae. Bonnie had purchased a beautiful three-bedroom two bath home. It was absolutely beautiful. We talked for a few. I met her future husband. They were driving to Jackson in order to take Janae to the train station. Janae spends her summers in Chicago with her father. I jumped back on 20 West, and I arrived home around 5:30pm. I stopped at the Kroger on 820 and Camp Bowie, bought some fried chicken and Sangria. I came home, took a shower, put on pajamas, ate chicken, drank wine and watched a movie. This is what I call living.

William called on Tuesday and invited me out to dinner. We met at Boomer Jack’s again. This time I had the wings. William sat across from me, but quickly jumped from his side of the table and sat next to me. William said he was not hungry, but he started eating some of my food. I do not like to share my food. What is up with people who say they are not hungry but will eat your food? At any rate, the date went smoothly. What I needed more than anything was to laugh. William made me laugh and laugh hard. We walked back to our cars hand in hand. He liked to lead and allowed him to.

We stood by our cars not wanting to leave but it was getting late. I told him that I was listening to some music and found us a theme song. I went to YouTube and found “While We’re Young” by Jhene Aiko. We slow danced in the parking lot as people walked by smiling. I don’t know where this is going but I am going to enjoy this unfolding story. I want to enjoy being with a man. I will participate in this narrative at least for a little while. The song ended and we went our separate ways. I liked that he opened my car door and waited for me to leave. I liked that he texted to make sure I arrived home safely. This is our second date but I like William Antoine Smith. His personality was relaxed and fun.

Chapter 9

I woke up to an alert. It was a dreamy White guy. He had muscles and everything. I had to put my glasses on in order to get a better look at him. In my Hattie voice, "That right there is nice."

Stephen201: Hi beautiful. You are dreamy. I am currently deployed. I would like to hear from you. My email address is… I look forward to hearing from you.

I checked out his profile. This is a good-looking White man. I'm down with the swirl. At this rate, I prefer a White guy. I drafted an email.

From: Lisa Davis

To: Stephen201

May 27, 2018 @ 7:14 PM

Hi,

It's Lisa from POF. How are you? Are you in the military or civilian? Thank you for your service. I will be praying for you and all personnel who are currently deployed.

You reside in Maryland? I saw that as your home state??

From: Stephen201

To: Lisa Davis

May 27, 2018 @ 10:44 PM

Hi Lisa,

How are you today, thanks for your prayers, happy to know you appreciate the work we are doing over here, you are so beautiful. I would really like to know you more.

Let me quickly write you a little about myself, my name is Stephen. I am 50 years old, a Major in the military, I live in Dallas Texas, I moved from Maryland to Dallas. I am presently deployed to Iran on a peacekeeping mission, I am on a special mission here, I have been here for 6 months. I will be home in four weeks. I am divorced, I have a son named Dale, I know we don't know each other for now but with good and honest communication we can know more about each other. I look forward to reading your email soon, I hope you had a great weekend.

Enjoy the rest of your evening.

From: Lisa Davis

To: Stephen201

May 28, 2018 @ 9:15 AM

Hi Stephen. I'm great and you? I pray because I understand. I spent time in the military and was deployed to the Middle East.

You are handsome. How old is your son? Mine are over 20. I'm 50. I don't have a problem getting to know you.

I work for a Social Services Agency. I work a lot. I love, love, love going to movies. I can't swim but love going near a beach or lake just to look at the water.

On your profile, it states Maryland. I was happy to see Dallas, TX as your hometown. I would love to meet you. I can guarantee you I will still be single in four weeks. This internet dating is not working for me.

From: Stephen201

To: Lisa Davis

May 28, 2018 @ 5:42 PM

Hello Lisa, thanks for your lovely message, wow its interesting you have been in the military, Dale is 16, you have two children that's great.

You are a very beautiful please do not over work yourself ok we still need you lol. I could teach how to swim it will be a great pleasure, I live in Texas, but I love it out there in Maryland, really 4 weeks is not long, thanks for the assurance that is the sweetest thing I have ever heard in a love time. I can't wait to be back home, surely its gonna work out for us... I am doing my report now, I hope to read your message shortly ok... enjoy the rest of your day.

From: Lisa Davis

To: Stephen201

May 28, 2018 @ 7:19 PM

Why is a handsome guy like you single? It was easy to meet someone when I served. I had to beat guys off me with a stick whenever I was in the military. It's been difficult for me to date because too many men (women) are nursing their wounds. Some people can't get over their exes and bring all of that luggage into the new relationship.

I'm not giving up on love. I believe in love. I've been single for several years. I'm patiently waiting on the man who will be perfect for me. I've never dated a Caucasian but have always been open to it. I was angry when George Clooney married Amal. The nerve of him. Caucasian men stare at me but have not asked me out. Oops, I almost forgot. One guy asked me out, but he stood me up. Lol. Oh, and the other one lied about his height

Hey, even if we don't make a love connection. I always like meeting new friends. I hope we will be able to meet after you return.

From: Stephen201

To: Lisa Davis

May 29, 2018 @ 10:44 AM

Hello darling. Why is a beautiful lady like you single? LOL how are you today, I am single because I haven't met the right one for me, women I meet only want sex and have fun, yes I want all that too but not just with anybody, I want someone for me, special, someone I can love and be loved in return, a lover and best friend, when I leave this horror here, I want to come home to have peace, have a family again and be happy, that is my only wish, and all that will not be complete without a soul mate.

I am glad you believe in love, I do too, that is the reason I decided to search again, I am ready to love despite all that as happened in the past, I would love us to make a love connection, I am very much interested in you, I believe we are adults and should know what we want when we see them. Hopefully, we can meet when I return. Kisses

From: Lisa Davis

To: Stephen201

May 29, 2018 @ 11:28 AM

Hello Handsome,

I'm single because I won't give up the "cookie" on the first or second date. I would like to be in a stable relationship before falling into bed because a guy bought my dinner. I want a man who wants me. I want someone who can make love to me with my clothes on. Sex is easy. How do we resolve conflict? I want a relationship in the living room before we make it to the bedroom. I desire that friendship whereas we should be able to talk about anything without picking each other apart. When I love, I love hard. I just want someone who loves me back. That's difficult to find.

What's your favorite color, cologne, food, drink, television show etc?

What's your favorite thing about a woman? What's a deal breaker for you? Do you have a sense of humor?

I will probably continue to ask questions just to get to know you better.

From: Stephen201

To: Lisa Davis

May 29, 2018 @ 5:13 PM

Oh, wow think I have found my dream girl, well never believed women like you are still out there, women I meet always want to have sex on the first date, well after reading your mail I feel we are on the same page, and meeting you is for a reason. When I fall in love... I fall deep, love is a beautiful thing when we find the right person, reading your mail gives me so much joy, seriously I feel I have met the one.

My favorite color is Blue, cologne is Creed Aventus. It runs about $200 but it is worth it. I love seafood, I am not a tv person, I prefer music, well I like my woman's hair to look good and nice, I do have a sense of humor, surely you won't be bore when you are with me well the major deal breaker is dishonesty. You can ask whatever you want darling, I also would know how you spend free time, do you like kisses, cuddling, what is your greatest turn off.

I am already looking forward to meeting you I feel so excited, thanks for brining smile back to my face.

From: Stephen201

To: Lisa Davis

May 31, 2018 @ 11:19 AM

Good morning sweetheart, how are you today I am glad I have access to reaching you, though it is limited because I would love to see you on cam and things like that, I can only wish for time to run fast so we can meet soon, I like peace of mind, I think we have a lot in common and you are very sweet, I would like to see more photos of you.

Now to your questions, I prefer wine, I like merlot and sauvignon. for cram coco butter, I don't think I have a favorite song, we could have a romantic dinner with candle lights and a bottle of champagne. I follow my heart and that's how I found you I will correct my mistakes and make better decision next time. I don't have friends my best friend died several years ago due to an IED blast. I have some men I talk to but can't call them friends, my son is my only friend until I met you. Family is everything to me, I will give everything to have once again, one filled with love, joy and happiness. I hope your morning started off well. I hope to hear from you soon.

From: Lisa Davis

To: Stephen201

June 1, 2018 @ 3:15 PM

Good Day To You,

How are you? I hope all is well. I don't have Skype or cameras set up. So, we have to do it like the old days.........write.

I'm asking all the questions. I will tell you I have several favorite songs. On any given day you will hear me say "that's my favorite song". I like chocolate ice cream. Sangria or Moscato are my choices of wine. After a rough day, maybe a Jack & Coke. I follow my heart. I've learned not to take things personally during this dating process. I have learned to laugh when a guy no longer responds. Regardless of what happens, I have refused to become bitter. I will be open to love over and over again. It will eventually manifest. Friendship is everything to me. At the root of any relationship is a solid friendship.

I enjoy communicating with you. I used to look forward to emails when I was in Iraq. Sorry for the loss of your best friend.

Any siblings? What about your parents? I won't badger you with too many questions. Heck, I'm an Investigator. Asking questions comes naturally.

Well, I had to reach out. Thinking of you and the rest of the service members. I pray God protects each and every one of you and bring you back home safely.

From: Stephen201

To: Lisa Davis

June 1, 2018 @ 7:15 PM

HI angel how are you, good to read your message again, you always make my day, it's fine we can write, I don't have access to Skype and all that too you know how it is over here, I will definitely like to share jack and coke with you, and I am not the guy would turn back half way, I want to be your man, my intentions are good and will make you happy.

My parents died 9 years ago, one-month interval guess they were so much in love, that is the love I seek, love that will never die. You sound like a professional, how many years have you served? I wanna go shower and have some food... I will be looking forward to your mail soon sweetie.

From: Lisa Davis

To: Stephen201

June 1, 2018 @ 11:01 PM

Hola,

How is my Rockstar? I'm about to throw away Denzel Washington and Keanu Reeves for you, just kidding.

I hope you are having a safe and wonderful day.

From: Stephen201

To: Lisa Davis

June 1, 2018 @ 3:00 AM

Hi my Angel. You know Katy Perry and Rihanna got nothing on you sweetie I threw them away the day I met you hahahhaa, You are beautiful baby, take it from me, I love this photo wish I could give you a hug and kiss right now... we are back from patrol.. anticipating your reply soon honey...

To: Lisa Davis

From: Stephen201

June 2, 2018 @ 9:00 AM

Lol, sure you did! Are you kidding me? I love Rihanna and Katy Perry. You can keep them.

I'm sorry about your parents. I hope y'all stay safe on patrols. I was telling my coworkers about you, and they sparked fear in me. I hope you aren't ISIS trying to recruit me because that won't happen.

I hope you aren't cat fishing me either. I hope you are Stephen "Rockstar" Hamilton who resides in TX and has 14yo prince. I've corresponded with other guys from POF. They lie like rugs. They lie and are schemers. You are OCONUS and your emails are consistent. I like consistency. At any rate, I went on one date before connecting with you and we went our separate ways. I'm tired of the games. It's exhausting. I'm writing a book about the game's men play! I could say people but I'm writing from a female perspective. Seriously, I'm in the process of writing my second book and I've gathered a lot of material. The book will be pure comedy.

At any rate, I will enjoy corresponding with you until we meet or not. I will look forward to the next response from you.

I can only pray that you are who you say you are. If not, I know how to do an about face and run.

Well, Rockstar. Be safe.

From: Stephen201

To: Lisa Davis

June 2, 2018 @ 3:00 PM

Hi sweetheart, how are you doing today, we just got back from patrol, lol it's funny how your co-workers could do so much and make you regard me as Isis? It is funny but a bit sad, I understand anyways, I am not cat fishing you. I take risk to message you every day. I am not supposed to using this computer for my personal business.

I could help in your books I have plenty of contacts in publishing and marketing. I think about you more than you know. I am not one of those men on POF, your messages has been sweet but this one is filled with bitterness and sarcastic, maybe that's your other side or your co-workers caused but I can only plead with you to be straight forward to me, I do not want to be led on. I am already into you. And I just hope you are too.

Have a great weekend.

From: Lisa Davis

To: Stephen201

June 3, 2018 @ 2:50 PM

Hi,

Bitterness & Sarcasm??? Negative. One thing you will get to know about me is I appreciate the ability to agree to disagree. It was a joke that I should not have shared. My coworkers are supportive and excited for me. Oh boy this is sad. It is my desire not to be catfished. That's not negativity.

Communication via email can get lost in translation. I want us to be able to talk about anything good, bad or ugly; big or small. I told you I want someone I can talk to, and we not pick each other apart. It can be done. Don't read too much into the previous email. I look forward to your emails and look forward to meeting you. If not, life goes on. Take care and stay safe

From: Lisa Davis

To: Stephen201

June 3, 2018 @ 10:00 PM

Hi,

I missed you today. I hope all is well. You don't have to respond if you are turned off due to the previous emails. I hope this will give you some insight.

I have realized that most of us fail in relationships because we want to remain in a euphoric state of feelings. If it feels good; I'm happy. If it doesn't feel good; I'm no longer interested. I understand feelings are fleeting. Feelings come and go. I may not feel like going to work but I go. Many of us don't "feel" what the other person is saying so we move on hoping to meet someone who will make us feel good.

I'm speaking for me. I no longer hold anyone responsible for how I feel. I'm happy daily. I choose to be happy. Sure, I have moments of sadness but I don't stay there.

Relationships are not the absence of conflict or disagreements; the key is how we respond to the conflict and disagreements. Today, I told my son that I desire a man who will like all sides of me because I'm willing to do that for the man I meet.

I've learned peace is not the absence of a storm. It's how you go through the storm that is a true test of faith and character. I've noticed men and women retreat and move on at the first sign of conflict. We never get to know a person before we move on to the next and the next looking for perfection.

I don't require perfection. I have enjoyed communicating with you. Thanks for the conversation and God bless.

That was the last conversation between Stephen and I. Women are not the only ones who are wounded or emotional.

William and I talked for about one month. We had gone out to dinner several times. I felt safe with him. I decided I would invite him over for dinner and a movie.

I called, "Hey. How are you?"

"Fine and you?" replied William.

"What are you doing Friday night?" I asked.

"Nothing that I can think of."

"Why don't you come over for dinner and a movie?" He replied, "That would be nice."

"Around 7:45pm", I said.

"Sounds great. See you then."

"Later" I said. Wait. I invited him for dinner as if I was going to cook. I hate cooking.

I sent a quick text 'What would you like to eat. I'm thinking wings and wine or bring whatever you like to drink?'

William's response 'Wings are good. I like quesadillas too.'

Friday arrived and I went to work as planned. I let Tara know William was coming over for dinner and a movie. Tara and I hoped I did not get any cases. If so, I will have to cancel dinner. As fate would have it, I did not have to conduct a family assessment; therefore, I did not have to cancel our dinner. I stopped by Applebee's and ordered food to go. I ordered a double order of hot wings and quesadillas. I stopped by Redbox and grabbed a couple of movies. I chose "Proud Mary" starring Taraji P. Henson and "Creed" starring Michael B. Jordan. That young man is fine. I can watch Creed over and over again. Plus, I like Sylvester Stallone. I arrived home and put my Sangria in the freezer.

At any rate, time was moving along. Fear began to creep in. My mind started racing. What if William is the killer? God, I pray he is not the killer. Is it too late for me to back out? Pull yourself together Let Monica and Tina know that he is coming over. Take a picture and text it to them. If he attacks, always go for the scrotum or the eyes. Keep your keys and ink pen nearby just in case I have to stab him. I'm strategizing now. Don't put on anything sexy. Society always blames women if something happens. Should I back out? Oh Lord. Warring angels and angels of protection cover me. It is 7:50p and no William. He is late. I am time oriented. My grandmother groomed me that way. She trained us to be on time. Time is important or time does not wait for no one she would often say. One of my favorite people has a quote that further cultivated my thoughts about time…..Minister Malcolm X said, "I have less patience with someone who doesn't wear a watch than with anyone else, for this type is not time conscious. In all our deeds, the proper value and respect for time determines success or failure." Malcolm X is an under celebrated historical figure. Between Laura and Malcolm X; I grew up believing everyone should be on time. Plus, I do not like stereo types. Whenever I hear, WE meaning Black folks are on "CP" time; that makes me cringe. I loathe stereotypes. If Wypipo say it, I defy it. At any rate, you get the picture. I expect people to keep their word, especially as it relates to time.

It is 8:00pm and William just pulled up. He texted and asked me to open the gate. I reluctantly opened the gate. I opened the door and snarled as he walked up the stairs to my apartment. I watched him scroll up to the door and thought he has no respect for time. I shook off this minor irritation. I looked down and he was not wearing a watch. Clutches pearls. He is horrible. No watch. Ugghhh. He is not much of a dresser either. He wears a lot of athletic gear. I am not going to try to change the way he dresses. That is his style. Another thing I noticed he does not have any etiquette. The first time you are invited to a person's home, it is customary to bring a gift. He brought Vodka and Grapefruit juice. He did not bring a customary gift. Humph. He was born and raised in Fort Worth. These folks are a little different. I should not expect much. True Southerners have etiquette. I smiled and said come inside and welcome to my abode. I invited him to have a seat on the sofa. I stared at his attire and shook my head not in a negative way. At least he is true to who he is. He does not dress to impress. I on the other hand is a fashionista. Since I am not going to buy him any clothes, there is no use complaining about the way he dresses.

I showed him my movie choices. We watched "Proud Mary" first. He talked and narrated the movie. I cannot stand anyone talking and tearing a movie to shreds. This one is a talker. I'm glad I had already seen the movie. Aside from him not appreciating a good movie, he was funny. He was thoroughly entertaining. I did not allow this distraction to irritate me. I put Creed in the DVD player. We fixed our drinks and carried our food into the living room. I pushed play and the second movie of the night began. Again, William talked and talked.

William said, "I have been to that restaurant in Philly. They have the best Philly cheesesteaks."

He went on non-stop talking about traveling to Philadelphia and other cities. At that point, I realized stopping the movie would be best. He said "I'm a sports fan. Let's watch the NBA playoffs. I turned to ESPN and we watched the Boston Celtics and Philadelphia 76ers. In between commercials, William said he is a big fan of the New Orleans Saints. Well, so am I. At least we have one thing in common.

William wanted me to make a video with him saying hey sucka in order to send it to one of his favorite cousins. We made a video, but it was too dark. At that point, William was holding his phone up so I can see the video and the name Carla popped up on the screen. He said, "Uh oh." We are not a couple, but I will make a mental note of that name. He put his phone away after that.

Apparently, both of us fell asleep on the sofa. I woke up at 3:30am and told him he had to go. He asked if he could sleep on the sofa, and I said no. He left. I locked the door and set my alarm. I crawled into bed and slept peacefully. I woke up around 10 am the following morning. William had called and texted. I returned his call. "Good morning. How are you?"

He said, "I am good. I am at work. I have to fix some software and do some data processing for some customers".

"How long have you been doing this type of work?"

"Oh, I have been doing this for eight years. I have had several jobs and I do not like working for anyone. I can't stand anyone telling me what to do."

The warning light flashed. *Warning, Warning. Pride. Pride. Pride.* He reminded me of Derek. Derek did not like anyone telling him what to do. Is this a man thing or is this a pride thing? My stomach turned. "Well, I will let you get back to work."

He asked, "What are you up to today?"

"I am going to Trader's Village." Traders Village is a big flea market in Grand Prairie, TX. You can buy almost anything there.

William said, "I will talk to you later."

True to his word, William called me later that night. He and his boys were hanging out. That was impressive. William took the time to say hi. That was kind of him. We chatted for a few minutes and that was it. I told him to enjoy his boys. He called Sunday morning and said he was going to work his part-time job. He delivered food for Uber Eats. A man working two jobs is an admirable quality. William was consistent and kept his word. If he said he was going to call, he did. He did not respond to text messages quickly, but he responded. Weeks went by and William began saying he wanted to get me off the dating site.

"No, I am not trying to get off the site yet. We are not a couple", I said.

"I don't want you on the dating site."

"We met on the dating site and now it is a problem".

He laughed. "NO, it is not a problem. I just want us to date exclusively". He said, "I am tired of this dating cycle. I just want to settle down." This conversation sounded all too familiar.

Two months into dating, he confessed that he did not have a lot of money. He owned his car, home and everything in it. But he was struggling financially. I don't know if he knew it or not, I had already picked up on the fact that he was financially challenged.

William said, "I don't meet any good women. The women I meet are rotten."

I looked up to heaven and said, "Not again. Not another victim. "What men do not know, I do not feel sorry for them and those lies. It is all lies. Men use that line for sympathy. They try to paint themselves as good men. It's all lies.

"When was your last serious relationship? Why did it end?" I asked.

"My last relationship was two years ago. She cheated on me," he said. I rolled my eyes yet again. *Oh Lord. Let the games begin.* I'm not any better because I began feeding into his lies.

"Shut up. What happened?"

"She was just rotten. My family tried to tell me she was not any good, but I did not listen. She was whorish and narcissistic. We were engaged but she married shortly after we broke up".

"Oh, you told me about this. Sorry, I forgot." I actually had forgotten about that tad bit of information.

"You have dated since that breakup, correct?"

"Yea, I have dated but nothing too serious. A lot of women are out here trying to play a man's game."

"It is not a man's game. It is a game of selfishness, brokenness, fear and trauma. Men who cheat are broken too."

Silence. I continued "Have you healed from the trauma?"

He snapped, "Hell yeah. That wench was not any good. Why would I be holding on to that?"

"Because men do not have the ability to bounce back after they have been cheated on. Y'all can dish it but absolutely cannot take it. A man's world ends after his woman cheats."

"I did not care" was his response but deep down I knew he was not being honest. He was still mentally, emotionally and spiritually connected to that woman. I know he cheated first but she got the best of him. Good for her I smiled inwardly. I love women who do these men in. I should not say that, but I secretly admire those women who break these jokers down. I shall call them Delilahs.

He was a nice guy, but he was "too nice". Something was not right about him.

The following day I called, "Hey sucka. What is going on?" He laughs every time I call him sucka.

"Nothing. Sitting in my chair watching television."

"I was thinking. How did you handle your fiancée cheating? What makes you angry?"

"What do you mean how did I handle it? I let her go. I have not heard from her since. When I am done, I am done."

Oh Lord. He sounds just like Derek. Lord, are all men the same or just the ones I meet? I can't deal with another familiar spirit.

He continued, "I don't get angry anymore. What's the point?"

"Well, how do you resolve conflict"

"I try to avoid conflict. We can talk about whatever is going on and go from there. I do not like all of that arguing." He did not really answer the question. "I just want to be happy."

I said, "That frightens me because I hear that a lot. I want to be happy. I want to be happy. I don't want any drama. How can a person not have drama in a relationship? A relationship is comprised of two people with different views, ideas, opinions and God only knows what else. A relationship will NEVER be without conflict. It is how we handle the conflict or drama that will make or break the relationship. In my opinion, men and women are single because everyone wants to be happy. That word is deceiving many. It is impossible for another person to make someone else happy. Absolutely impossible." The silence between us was loud.

William invited me to his home the following Friday. I did not take him a gift. I'm learning how to do unto others as they do unto me. His home was extremely clean. I also recognized a woman's touch. He never verbalized that his ex-decorated, but a woman knows. There were too may feminine pictures, flowers and colors in the home. The house was cute and quaint. According to William, his family built the home in the 1970s. After his parents died, they left the home to him and his sisters. All of his sisters are married so the home is his. He said he only had to pay the taxes, insurance and utilities. If he was a smart man, he should be stacking coins.

I contacted my cousin Monica on FaceTime in order for her to see his face and his surroundings. I want to make sure someone saw him just in case he is the killer.

We chatted with her for a little while. William was in the process of making a homemade cheeseburger. He asked if I wanted one which I declined. I ate before going to his home. We talked about his sisters and his childhood. We did not talk about anything serious. William was more focused on laughing and having fun. William lives to laugh and have fun. I like fun too, but sometimes I like to have serious conversations. I will just go along to get along.

Like many people, William did not have cable. He said he did not watch a lot of television. He had a firestick. We listened to the blues and talked. I went home around midnight.

Three months into the "situationship," I spent the night with William. On Saturday morning, we ate breakfast and decided to do nothing. I sat on one end of the sofa reading while he watched 48hrs on the firestick. Shortly afterwards, he asked if I had seen "Power." Power is a popular show on Starz. It stars that beautimous Omari Hardwick and Naturi Naughton. This show is really good. I have cable but do not have Starz. I may have to call Spectrum and add Starz just for this show.

We could not enjoy the show because William's phone was ringing off the hook. Between the phone and text message alerts, we were both distracted. He made sure his phone was not close to him. I was observing him. He was tense. He asked if I was hungry. He left to get us some food. Plus, I assumed he was going to return some of those missed phone calls. I packed up my belongings while he was gone. I wanted him to be free to answer his phone in his own home. We ate these juicy and delicious burgers with onion rings. The burger was so juicy I could not eat it all.

We resumed watching "Power". William appeared to be agitated. I told him I was going home. As soon as I arrived home, he called to say I did not have to leave. He wanted me to come back and watch more episodes of "Power".

"Man, you are reminding me of that evil ex-husband. I cannot stand that up and down behavior," I quipped.

"I am not up and down. I was sleepy and tried not to fall asleep on you. Please come back. I enjoy your company."

I drove back to his house and spent the night. I went to church from his house the following morning. It felt weird sleeping with a man, not having sex but actually sleeping with a man and getting dressed for church. I headed to church and William called to make sure I had arrived. He made sure to check on me here and there. Church was good. I stopped at Long John's Silver on Altamesa, grabbed a three piece with fries, coleslaw and headed home. I relaxed the rest of the day. William and I texted back and forth the rest of the day.

On Monday, Bonnie called and said she and her boyfriend were coming to Dallas. Larry wanted to celebrate his birthday. I don't know where to go around here. I'm not a huge fan of clubs. I called William and asked if he knew of any place that would be fun. He told me about R L's Blues Palace in Dallas. He said you have to reserve a table and get there early or else they would give your table away. I researched RL's on Google. That was an interesting concept. You can bring your own bottle and food. There is a band, DJ and dancing. This looks very interesting. I provided Bonnie with that information. She made the reservations for ten people.

This was our third month dating but something had shifted. I'm telling you that third month is when all of my relationships go south. William was not calling or texting as much. He would invite me over but was distant. He acted as if I was getting on his nerves. One Saturday morning, his cell phone rang. He answered. I heard a woman's voice. "I am going to call you back." He hung up abruptly.

I said, "It is 8 o' clock in the morning and she has not heard from you in a couple of days. She is starting to get worried."

"That was my nephew. I have a block on my phone, and no one can call me this early except certain family members."

Why did I know he was lying? That was not his nephew. That is why he does not sleep well at night. His demons are tormenting him. I decided to give William a break for a few weeks. I will reach out to him the closer it gets to Bonnie and Larry's visit. One week before Bonnie and Larry were scheduled to arrive, I reached out to William and asked if he was still going with us.

He said, "Why wouldn't I? You are the one that stopped talking to me?"

"You have plenty of women to talk to when I am not around," I said flatly.

Every time I took a break from him; I tried to meet other men. I know he was entertaining several women. I do not want to be faithful to a whore. I did not meet anyone.

Bonnie, Larry and their two children came to visit. We went out to eat at Rodeo Goat on Bledsoe St. I texted William and told him I would be ready around 7 pm and he can meet me at my place. I told him Bonnie is slow getting dressed and we will lose the table waiting on her. He agreed to meet me at my place around 7pm. I have not seen him in a few weeks. I was shocked to see him in jeans, a button-down Polo shirt and shoes. He typically wears athletic gear. We did not hug or anything. I talked to him as if I was talking to Tina or one of my girlfriends. I asked him to help me pick out shoes and accessories. He made himself a drink. We hopped on I-30 East to Dallas and forty-five minutes later we arrived at R L's Blues Palace. We found a parking spot and waited until 8pm to enter. William allowed me to enter first, not because he was a gentleman but because he did not have money to pay for the cover charge. I paid the $20.00 cover charge. It only cost $10.00 to get in. William is not as slick as he thinks he is. I knew he was broke. He is a user but right then we were using each other. I was really lonely after losing my brother. William was filling a void.

I won't focus on his slickster ways. I needed to enjoy my evening. We went to our table and sat down. Bonnie and Larry were late getting there. I think they arrived around 9pm or later. They brought Jack Daniel's Tennessee Whiskey, Crown Royal and some expensive brand of Tequila. One guy brought an assortment of wings from Boomer Jack's. William was drinking Vodka and grapefruit juice. We laughed, danced and had a good time. The more William drank, the more flirtatious he became. He was touching the woman at the next table. He was hugging the waitress who looked at me to rescue her. I shrugged my shoulders. She mouthed, "He is drunk, isn't he?" William walked over to this guy. He was standing between the male and female bathroom. He called me over and made introductions. William said he and the guy played football together in college. I went back to the table. Shortly afterwards, a woman was on her way to the bathroom. William and this woman were clearly flirting. I watched them flirt. Other women started looking at me like 'this dude is disrespecting you'. I shrugged my shoulders as if to say he is grown. William is the type who needs a lot of attention from women. I've paid attention to him over the past three months. Whenever we are out, his body language is saying look at me. He puffs out his chest and tries to seduce women with his eyes. I had seen him do it on multiple occasions. His body language was screaming "LOOK AT ME". He felt abandoned when all eyes were not on him. This woman was clearly giving him attention and he was enjoying it.

I began flirting with an attractive guy across the room. I walked by and grabbed his hand. I might as well. William was not worth two nickels rubbed together. Why get mad? I knew this wasn't going anywhere. Although I tried to flirt, no one took the bait. I suppose men were not going to entertain me because they did not want any part of that drama.

William is a whore. I'm going to ride it out until I cannot tolerate him any longer. In the meantime, I'm going to try and meet someone more stable and consistent than him. We enjoyed the rest of our evening. The club closed and we were hungry. We went across the street to Henderson's Chicken, but they did not have any seasoning. I suppose they use this seasoning that makes the chicken taste really good. The chicken was not bad. A little hot sauce would make it better. We could not figure out where to go and eat. As we were leaving, Larry noticed a man with a barbecue grill. We stopped in order for them to get some food. William went back to Henderson's and bought me and him two six-piece wings and fries. We dropped Bonnie and Larry off at the Hilton in downtown Dallas and headed back to Fort Worth.

He talked and talked about being a football star in high school and college. He talked about attending a predominately White college and sleeping with White girls. He talked about his many travels to Hawaii, Jamaica and other exotic places. He often talked about his cousin who was a famous singer. He loved talking about how all of the men traveled, and they were a part of his entourage. Poor thing is caught up with who he used to be and what he used to have. He is not yet a man. He is manly, but there is an unhealed boy waiting to catch up to the man he should be. He talked and talked. I sat in silence. I was wondering if I would ever meet a whole man. One who isn't consumed with his past, his past girlfriends, his past fiancé, his past career, his past financial status and the list goes on.

William was beginning to look more and more like Derek. I am not yet healed or whole because this familiar spirit is sitting next to me. We made it back to my place. He was drunk and talking loudly! Gosh he is loud. I was hoping he fell asleep soon. I'm almost positive my neighbors can hear him. What do we see in each other? I can speak for me. I am dealing with loneliness and grief. What is his problem? He does not drink often but when he does, he gets wasted. I suppose both of us are broken. We were going to play around with each other's brokenness until one of us gets tired. He continued talking and eating. I begged him to go to sleep. He fell asleep while I stared at the back of his head. I was wondering what I saw in him. He talks but does not communicate. He is hung up on his ex. Maybe I like him because he is emotionally unavailable, and I know this will fizzle out really soon. Maybe I want this to self-sabotage. I don't have a clue, but he is not this "good man" he wants to be.

On Sunday morning, Bonnie wanted me to meet them at Trader's Village. William finally woke up with a hangover I might add. I gave him an Ibuprofen and bottle of water.

He said, "Man, I need to stop drinking."

"You need to but you won't," I chuckled. "You are drinking to hide something. Something is not right with you." William did not respond.

He asked, "Did we have sex last night?"

"Absolutely not. Your drunk behind fell asleep as soon as your head hit the pillow."

"What are you getting ready to do?"

"Bonnie wants me to meet them at Trader's Village," I said.

"I would go but I have to go home and work," he stated.

I began making jokes in my head. He is always working but never has any money. I chuckled when I compared William to Tommy from "Martin." *You ain't got no job Tommy.* He is always working on this program or installing software, but he never has any money. I feel sorry for him. His mind tells him he is rich, but in reality, he is broke. I want to see him succeed. He is extremely intelligent, but he is a hustler.

William ate the rest of his chicken, got dressed and went home. I jumped on I-20 east and drove to Trader's Village. I caught up with Bonnie and her clan. It is hot as fish grease out here. I'm glad I wore all white. I cannot stand this heat. I'm "ret-to-go". This is a catch phrase from Ugly Wanda played by Jamie Foxx on "In Living Color". Wee doggie it is hot out here and Bonnie is looking for a rug. Bonnie does not seem to be phased by the heat. I feel sweat in places where there should not be any sweat. If hell is hotter than Texas, I am not going. We walked up and down endless aisles. Bonnie did not find what she was looking for.

I was so happy when she said, "I do not see what I am looking for we might as well get on the road."

I was elated. We hugged and said our goodbyes. I hopped in that Altima and jumped back on 20 west and brought it on back to Fort Worth. I could not wait to hop in the shower again.

I washed that heat and sweat right off my body. I slid into my pajamas and flopped down on my sofa. Yay God. This is living. I watched a Lifetime movie and relaxed. I tried to relax as much as possible because God only knows what fresh kind of hell awaits me on Monday morning. I talked to my best friend Tina for most of the evening. I told her how William was flirting right in front of my face. I tried to flirt with other men but I could tell they did not want to be bothered with that drama. I can't blame them. Tina and I laughed.

I said, "Girl, this dude ain't worth a darn. You know how all of the signs are there but you stay in the mess."

"I understand," she said. Who am I to judge? You know my history," she reminisced.

One thing I can say about Tina. She is supportive. It does not matter what you tell her, she has your back. She never makes me feel less than or dumb. She is always ready to fight someone on my behalf. We continued talking and I told her I needed a drink. I did not drink a lot last night because I knew I was going to be the designated driver. Tina stayed on the phone with me while I drove down Camp Bowie to Como. I went to the Eskimo Hut in order to get a daiquiri. I bought an extra-large Barb Marley with four extra shots. We talked for five or six hours.

By now, I am tipsy.

I fell asleep around 10pm but woke up around 3 am. I had a stomachache from the daiquiri. Not that it wasn't good, it was too sweet. This voice kept whispering, "He is no good for you."

"Let him go."

Every time I wanted to let him go, my cousin Monica and friend Brittany would say they think he is good for me. Both carry a prophetic mantle, so I allowed their voices to drown out the voice that was speaking to me.

Chapter 10

I knew that there was something off about him, but I cannot figure it out. He is the type of "good man" that as long as he is in my face and is nice to me and that is his definition of a "good man". When he is with another woman, he is a "good man" to her. In his eyes, he is good as long as he is ignoring all of the other women while he was with you. This is straight out of the Player's Handbook.

Dang it, right, wrong or indifferent all I want is six months. The longest relationship I have been in was five years. We know how that ended. That was a hot mess. I'm going to make it to six months with William even if it is raggedy. God knows it is raggedy. You can tolerate his whorish assets for six months. You already know what you are dealing with so you can do it *(in my water boy voice)*.

I knew I was out of order, but I am tired of being alone, especially after my brother passed away. I spent a lot of time at William's house because I have been cooped up in my apartment for five years. Going to his house broke up my routine. I spent a lot of weekends at his house. On Sunday mornings, I still went to church. I enjoy William's company, but he is too sneaky. I have my own insecurities, but something is not right. He invited me to his nephew's graduation but failed to call on the day of the graduation. I shared with Monica that he is inconsistent. Monica encouraged me to be patient with him because we are in the "early" stages of dating. She advised me to cut him some slack because right now I needed someone to keep me company. Monica stated, "Maybe he forgot to call you or maybe he was waiting on you to call him in order to confirm that you wanted to go to the graduation."

"I said yes when he asked. Am I supposed to keep confirming? I am confused."

She said, "Just cut the man some slack."

I did not reach out to him. A few days later he called and talked as if everything was normal. I could not avoid the issue.

"Um, how was your nephew's graduation?"

"It was good. We went back to the house for a small gathering. I stayed for a little while and went home."

"I was waiting on you to tell me where I was supposed to show up and a time."

"I did not think you wanted to go because you did not bring it up again."

"You invited me, and I said, okay. I even went out and bought a nice dress, but you never gave me a specific time or place."

"It was a miscommunication," he said.

In my mind, I had painted William as a liar. I know I am right.

Monica called, "How is William?"

"He is alright. I feel it deep down in the pit of my stomach that he is.... I won't say it out loud."

I told her about the miscommunication. Of course, Monica justifies his behavior. I just can't be with another lying wonder. Due to my profession, I am around lying wonders all day long. It is draining. I do not feel like being around a 'lying wonder' in my spare time. I need stability.

Against my better judgment, I decided to keep talking to him. I told him I was not ready for a relationship. I shared the verbal abuse I had endured and the lying men I have been around. I would like an almost honest man. I think it is too much to expect complete honesty from a man. Just like near beer, I would like a near honest man. I just tickled myself. If a man is honest, he was usually abrasive. It is a fine line but I expect a little more truth than I have gotten.

William explained, "I am not trying to hurt you. I know what that feels like. I want a relationship. I'm tired of playing games. I'm not trying to use you. You are a nice person. Give us a chance because I am getting attached to you." We mutually agreed to move forward and to give dating a try.

I try to watch Saturday Night Live every weekend unless it is a rerun. I have not heard from William since earlier that day. I was lying in the bed laughing as Alec Baldwin does an awesome job imitating Trump. This show cracks me up. Around 11:30pm, my phone rings and it is William. I hear background noise. I guess he had friends over. "Hey bae. How you doing?"

"I am great, and you sound like you are feeling good."

He says, "I am. I was thinking about you. I was thinking we are not getting any younger, we might as well go ahead and do this. I want to take care of you. I can save you some money. My house is paid for. You won't have to pay any rent. I can't do much for you but at least you can save all of the money you are paying in rent. I will continue paying the bills that I have. Your children will be welcome here too. I am tired of being by myself. I can tell you are a good woman. I want to be with you. I will protect you. I won't try to use you. I am a good man. I think I can marry you."

"Sure William. That sounds good. You have been drinking. We will see if you remember those words when you are sober."

"I was thinking about you and wanted to let you know how I feel. I will talk to you later."

"Good night, Sucka."

"Good night, bae."

A drunk man tells the sober truth. It's probably on his mind but he is afraid of commitment.

I went to church on Sunday. He called after I got out of church.

"Hi, how was church?"

"Good as always. Pastor Womack teaches in a way that a child can learn. I need that type of teaching. How are you?" I asked.

"I am good. I am going to work for a couple of hours," he said.

"So, do you remember all of the beautiful words you spoke on last night?" I asked.

"What did I say?" He inquired.

"You said you will protect me; save me some money and you think you could marry me." I repeated.

"I meant it. Life is short. We only have twenty more good years before it all ends. Jesus is coming back soon. We might as well do this and enjoy each other," he continued.

"We shall see," I said incredulously.

After his confession of love and possible marriage, he began flirting more. He claimed he was not big on flirting via text, but he was consistent with calling. Occasionally, he would check on me or send a flirty text. He called morning, noon and night. I liked and hated it at the same time. I liked the attention but knew it was a matter of time before the "newness" wore off and he would no longer call or text. I knew I was right. I wanted to be wrong because a small piece of me liked him but I knew I was right.

William lived close to my office. I had begun spending a lot of time at his house. He told me to leave some of my products and clothes at his house. I left hygiene products and make up at his house. I did not want to leave a lot because there were still products from his last relationship or current relationship.

Our arrangement worked out for a while. I work in social services. Social Services is an underpaid, thankless, consuming and overwhelming profession. You give more than you get. You work more than forty hours per week with no overtime pay. You are constantly criticized by the higher uppers and the families we serve. Absolutely nothing you do is good enough. Mind you, the families we serve have mega problems. Many of them are in bondage but do not know it. Many are riddled with generational curses, poverty, lack of hope, lack of opportunities, poor decision making, no conflict resolution skills, lack of parenting skills, no family support, substance abuse, and domestic violence. Poor people are not the only ones who use social services. Rich people use it more and they can be horrible. They are entitled but cannot see their families are equally as jacked up as poor people.

Needless to say, I needed a stress reliever. At this particular time, William had become my addiction. William worked out occasionally. He tried to encourage me to work out too. I need to work out but it is not one of my favorite things to do. In order to relieve stress and break up the monotony of work, William said we are going bike riding. He said I needed to do something to get my mind off of work and my brother. I have not ridden a bike since I was a teenager. Hey, I am going for it.

After work, I went home, grabbed some work out gear and packed an overnight bag. I am actually going bike riding. William secured the bikes on the back of his car. We grabbed helmets, gloves and water. We proceeded to Trinity Park. This bike is so uncomfortable. It was too short for me. His ex had to be a short woman. I am 5'9" with long legs. It will have to do because I am here now. My legs and butt are burning as we rode through the park. It was a dangerous ride. People were walking in the spots that were clearly marked for bike riders. I am yelling for people to move out of the way. There are turns, twists and small bridges. I was not handling that bike it was handling me. I eventually tell William to go on. He rode ahead of me and I eventually caught up. I was walking/riding. I was soooo tired. We made it to this bench, and I told him I had to sit down. We sat down and talked. His phone rang, he would answer but his responses were always a quick "I'm going to call you right back."

"How many miles is this?" I wanted to know.

He said, "It was supposed to have been two miles, but it is actually five miles".

I screamed, "Five miles. I could have done two miles easily."

We arrived at the Fort Worth Stockyards. William said, "I wanted us to come to the Stockyards in order to have a drink and ride back."

"No sir. You are going to have to go back in order to get the car. I am not going to make it."

I was able to sit down while he rode back in order to get the car. I called Bonnie. "Hey, girl. I am sitting outside in the stockyards."

"What are you doing there?"

"Honey, William and I rode bikes down here. He wanted us to have a drink and ride back but baby it is dark now. We will be all night riding back. He is gone to get the car."

"I am going to stay on the phone with you until he gets back," she said.

It took William a long time to get the car. I am not crazy. I know he runs a business, but all of those calls were not business calls. I'm almost positive he has to do some damage control with a few ladies. Bonnie said, "I'm starting to get worried. He needs to come on."

"If he does not show soon. I will have to call a cab," I stated. William arrived and Bonnie said put me on speaker. "I thought I was going to have to come to Fort Worth. Don't mess with that one," she said matter-of-factly.

I was sweating and tired. I am finally in the car relishing under the air conditioner.

On the drive back, William and I tried to find something quick to eat. I wasn't really hungry, but I needed to put something on my stomach. I was exhausted. All I wanted to do was take a shower and go to bed. We went back to his house. William cooked some baked chicken and spinach. I didn't want any of that. I settled for some beef hot dogs on wheat bread. Who is this person? I like white hot dog buns. I ate and decided it was time to take a shower. I turned on the water and realize my body wash is not on the shower rack. I did notice Dove body wash and it was not mine. William only uses Dial soap. I screamed from the toilet, "William, where is my body wash?"

"You did not leave any body wash over here."

"Stop lying ninja. I left Orange Blossom body wash over here."

While I'm on the toilet, he enters the bathroom and finds my body wash. He'd hidden it in the back of the linen closet. At least he did not allow anyone else to use my body wash. I sat on the toilet shaking my head. I knew I was right. I showered and prepared for bed. I could not sleep. While he was sleeping, I started browsing the dating site for eligible men. This ticks me off. Men get to whore around, but we do not have a lot of choices. Folks tell women to get healed but men go from woman to woman.

The following morning, William was cooking breakfast. I did not want any of his food. I got dressed and told him I was not hungry. Plus, I wanted to get breakfast from Whataburger.

William said, "Stop acting crazy. It was cleaning products in that bottle." While finishing my make up, I smelled the body wash. I was definitely not cleaning products. I gathered all of my stuff. He begged me not to leave.

"I have separation anxiety," He confessed. I told him I was not in the mood to deal with what he was dishing out. I smiled and thanked him for his hospitality. I packed my stuff and left. I decided to give him space while I tried to meet someone else. I reflected on the prayer call that I listened to one night. It was hosted by Prophetess Tera Carrisa Hodges and Dana Reece. They are the ones who talked about circular dating. Prophetess Reece said, "Women should go out on multiple dates that way you won't be disappointed when that one guy you have poured your all into walks away." I hear her but where are all of these men? I most certainly would like to circular date. Williams's favorite line kept ringing in my ears "There are nine women to one man in Fort Worth which means it is easier for men to meet someone than women".

William called one week later. I referred to him as "Ms. Dove." I set up a profile on another dating site. Not the one where I met him. Heck, we are going to play together. Unfortunately, I was not getting any hits. After two weeks of no hits and no action, I was right back at his house. I think I really enjoyed being away from my apartment. Plus, there were times William catered to me and I needed to feel like a woman. He cooked dinner and invited me over. I spent the night. The following morning, he was cooking breakfast. He was on the phone telling a friend that it feels good to have someone in his life. He was tired of being alone. His friend called out the name of another woman. William said, "No, Lisa. You have not met her." I took a shower and got dressed for work. Again, William asked me to try again. He asked me to leave more stuff at his house. He made space for my clothes and underwear. He also gave me a key and code to his alarm.

William and I began spending more and more time together. I left pajamas, slippers, a few dresses, make up, an extra charger, hygiene products and a bottle of my favorite perfume Daisy by Marc Jacobs. I secretly hoped he would not allow Ms. Dove or anyone to touch my stuff. I blatantly asked him not to allow anyone to wear or use my items.

There were moments Player Bill I meant William was very good. He cooked breakfast and dinner. I loved his grilled chicken wings. He did not have any money. He could not afford to take me places, but he did small things in order to show me that he was present. I loved the foot rubs. He taught me how to play spades. Don't judge me. I am 50 and just learned how to play spades.

I did not have any peace about him. I enjoyed his company, but I could tell he was not all the way invested. His heart belongs to someone else. Alton is emotionally unavailable. A part of him wants a relationship but he is still attached to the pain of his ex. No one can compete with a ghost. He tries to deny it but I can see it. At any rate, I am going to take this for what it is a "situationship".

I am going to live out this fantasy with William, I have never been on a trip with a man. I am fifty and have not had a lot of good experiences with men. I will pretend he is a good man, and I will enjoy this movie that I am directing in my head. I can journal about the experiences and write a book about it later. That is exactly what I will do.

Chapter 11

My first trip of the year was to California. My other trips will be traveling around Texas. One of the places I want to visit is Galveston. A few years ago, my cousin and I went on a cruise that sailed out of Galveston and that gave me the desire to want to go back. We did not see the city of Galveston. Somehow the GPS took us around the back of the city. I know Galveston has more to offer than what we saw. What can I say? I like being near water. I love water. One would think I can swim but I cannot. I love sitting on a beach overlooking the water. I like the way water flows unto the shore. Water is movement. Water cleanses. Water purifies. Water is calm until it's not.

I decided it was time for a road trip. I requested vacation for mid-July. I planned a four, day weekend to Galveston, TX. Of course, William is going with me. He can drive because I drive so much for work. It will be nice to stretch out and enjoy the ride. I told my neighbor I was planning a weekend getaway to Galveston. Ms. Ann, "Where are you staying?"

"I always stay at the Super 8 Motel."

"How much did you pay?"

Urgh? This heifer is nosey. I told her how much I had paid. "I wish you had told me. I have some points I need to use. Let me call and see if I can transfer the points to the Super 8. "First, are you going by yourself." "Sure." I lied. I still have to pay so what does it matter if I am going alone or not. As favor would have it, Ms. Ann was able to transfer her points. Instead of paying almost $400, I only had to pay $92 for four days and three nights.

In previous conversations, I had shared some of the things I wanted in a partner, mate, lover, and friend. If I pay for the hotel, I want the guy to pay for the gas. I just want to know the guy is present and not stingy. I don't know if my standards or expectations are low, but I don't know of too many men who pay for everything anymore. I don't know how to date or dating protocols. I just want someone to be my teammate and watch my blindside. We should be standing shoulder to shoulder and back-to-back. Antyhoo, I am going to see how William responds on this trip. William said, "Let's take the bikes. We can ride up and down the beach." "Sure. That sounds like fun." In my head I am thinking that sounds like a workout, but it might be fun. I told William I would be at his house by 10am or it depends on how well I sleep. I arrived at his home around 11am. We packed my car. He secured both bikes onto my car. I said a prayer for traveling grace and mercy. We turned onto South Freeway, merged onto I-35W South and then onto I-20 East towards Dallas. We arrived in Galveston around 4pm. The motel was a block and a half off the beach. We checked into the motel, and I could not wait to get to that water. We unpacked the car and headed to the beach. I should have been smart like William and worn shorts, but nope. I wore jeans and a t-shirt. I don't care. I am excited to be near this water. We walked east towards the water. I was so giddy. I saw this long pier to my right and another pier to my left with a huge Ferris wheel. I saw all of the people lounging in beach chairs, some were fishing, and some were on jet skis. I was so excited.

I rolled up my jeans and we walked hand in hand along the beach. The water came up to my calves and that was enough for me. The water was cold. I enjoyed watching the children play in the water, try to catch birds and build sandcastles. We walked out onto these big rocks that extended out into the water. I do not like to take pictures, but the scenery was just right. The beach reminded me of the Mississippi Gulf Coast, especially when I looked to the left and saw Landry's Seafood. We walked and walked before you know it, we were a mile and a half down the beach.

All of that walking made me hungry. I was hungry and hot. We took more pictures and headed back to the room. There was a Waffle House on the corner directly in front of our motel. We stopped and grabbed something to eat. There weren't any customers only the staff. I ordered a hamburger with grilled onions and jalapeños, and hash browns. William had a grilled chicken sandwich with smothered hash browns. He paid for our meal. I was looking to see if he was really stingy or just broke. I believe he was more broke than stingy. Waffle House was within his budget.

We went back to the room. I took a shower, read my bible and went to sleep. I woke up around 8:45pm and William was gone. I watched television. He entered the room and I asked him how come he let me sleep so long. I had plans to go back to the beach and site see. He said he knew I was tired and he wanted me to rest. He had been outside sitting by the pool and playing on social media. He fixed a drink, gave me a kiss and left the room. An hour passed and I decided to go downstairs by the pool. It was humid and muggy as heck out there. I waved to William. He jumped up and came over to where I was standing. There were a lot of people in the pull having a good time. William came over to where I was standing and gave me a kiss. He asked me to join him.

William said, "This is so cool. I am having fun watching these people have a good time. Do you see that kid? He and his friend were calling each other nigga and his dad looked at me and said sorry."

I looked at the family who were Hispanic. I said, "Maybe they are saying it because it is slang. They aren't calling you a nigger, right? They are playing around and calling each other nigga, right?"

"I am not bothered by it because these young kids think it is cool", he stated. "If the rappers were not broadcasting in every song and the culture would stop making it cool, we could put the word to bed. Until then, if TI, Two Chains, Jay Z and all others think it is hip, then what can I do," I say.

I shrugged my shoulders. "Well, I am not a fan of heat. I'm going back inside where it is cool."

William came inside, took a shower and we watched a movie. Around 10:30pm, both of us were hungry. The Waffle House was packed. We decided to find the local Walmart in order to buy some snacks. Before going to Walmart, we drove up and down the beach. This was so beautiful and peaceful. I'm actually out of town and on a trip with a guy. This is nice.

William and I drove around until we located Walmart. He and I bought sandwiches, popcorn, drinks and a blanket because the room is super cold. We headed back to the room, ate sandwiches and popcorn. Both of us fell asleep. On Friday morning, I went to the beach around 6:45am. I took my folding chair, Bible, water and phone. It was so peaceful and serene. The beach was relatively empty. I turned on praise and worship music, read the word and relaxed. I thanked God for being mighty, strong, perfect, creator, redeemer, restorer, and healer. I was in a zone. Around 8am, I heard a bunch of ruckus behind me. I hate to sound like I'm racist against my own people but here come the coloreds. It is too early to be that loud. I look around the beach which was relatively empty and wondered why they brought that noise directly behind me. I sat there and watched the waves. It is too early for this amount of noise. I pack up my belongings and headed back to the motel.

When I entered the room, William was in the process of waking up. I took a shower and relaxed. We got dressed, discussed our plans for the day and ate breakfast. Today, we are going to ride our bikes to the pier. That Ferris wheel is calling my name. It is hot out here but there is no turning back. I was exhausted by the time we made it to the pier. We locked the bikes onto a pole and walked up to the pier. These two women asked if we wanted their bracelets which we quickly accepted. We were able to enter the park for free. I watched families get on rides and they seemed to be enjoying themselves. My eyes locked on the Ferris wheel. William explained he was not going to get on a Ferris wheel. I asked him to escort me up the walk to the Ferris wheel. He did. He stood a little way back. The young lady operating the Ferris wheel told him I could not ride it alone. William reluctantly agreed. Other couples had gotten on and were seated. Some of them began encouraging him to just get on the ride. A few were even laughing. Upon entering the ride, William immediately grabbed the pole. I saw fear all over him. I was tickled.

William said, "I must really love you to do this."

"I appreciate you for riding with me," I said through laughter.

As the Ferris wheel went round and round, I was able to see all of the beauty Galveston offered. The ride finally ended. We walked back down the pier. William said that was his last time doing something like that. I thanked him for his service in between laughs. William wanted to ride this ride that looks like a swing. It goes really high and wide.

Absolutely not.

He said, "I rode the Ferris wheel with you, you can do this with me." I was thinking not this tit for tat crap. He was adamant about getting on that dang ride. I said a prayer and got in line. As we got closer to getting onto the ride, my heart was racing. William grabbed my hand and said, "Let's go." It turns out, he had no desire to ride the swing. He wanted to pay me back for dragging him onto the Ferris wheel. He found the couple who had previously laughed at him.

"Did y'all see how scared she was? I got her back."

I do not like this part of him. Unlike him, I can care less if people think I am afraid…….I was. We finally found a ride we both could agree on…cars. Since the cars were low, I thought they would be harmless. Boy, was I wrong….I was fine as long as we were going clockwise. When the cars went counterclockwise, I became sick to my stomach. This motion sickness is real. I was freaking sick. I closed my eyes and began thinking happy thoughts. The ride would end soon. As soon as the ride ended, my legs were wobbly. I felt like I had to vomit. I was weak and had to sit down. William bought me a bottle of water. I was literally sick to my stomach. God have mercy. We had to sit there for an hour before I could walk. I finally mustered up the strength to go the bathroom. It was hot, dirty and filthy. Why do we have to be so dang filthy? I finished my bottle of water. We walked back across the street and hopped back onto our bikes and rode back towards the motel. We stopped at Fish Tales and ate. When we walked inside the restaurant, a group of White guys were sitting at the bar singing "Proud to Be an American". They abruptly stopped when we walked in. We sat at the table facing the beach. The group of White men went to the patio leaving William, me, the waitress and bartender alone in the restaurant. Poor Wypipo. They really believe God gave them America and the rest of us are intruders. That is another story for another day. The waitress brought our food to the table. She tried to be polite. I suppose she was as polite as she could be to two people who did not look like her. I pray the cook did not spit in our food. The fish and chips were not the best, but I was hungry. William paid for our meal. So far so good.

I could not wait to get back to the room and take a shower. Believe it or not, I did not ride and walk. I rode back without giving up. I am exhausted. We finally made it back to the room. I'm hot and sweaty. Yuck. Both of us took showers, played on our phones and took a nap. Equalizer 2 had just come out. I don't care how tired I am, I have to see this movie. I love Denzel Washington. We took a nap and headed to see the movie at Galveston Premiere 11 West Beach. The theater was small but relatively clean. I was smiling like a kid in a candy store. William fell asleep as soon as the movie came on. I did not care. I was watching my main man. The movie was awesome. As we walked towards the exit, a random movie goer began talking about the movie. He asked, "How did you like the movie?"

"It's Denzel, he can do no wrong in my eyes."

"I cannot believe they put Denzel in the second movie. It was an older white guy in the first Equalizer," the stranger said matter of factly.

"I am the ultimate Denzel fan and that does not make any sense. Apparently, you did not see the first one because Denzel was in that one."

This random movie goer wanted to debate me. I conceded. I know all of Denzel's movies and he starred in the first Equalizer. I walked away because I was slightly perturbed.

William laughed as we walked back to the car.

He joked, "That man was getting under your skin. He does not know you love Denzel."

I rolled my eyes. I feel like that Wayans girl from "In Living Color". She used to say best nobody talk, about Ms. Jenkins. I feel the same way about Denzel. Best nobody talk about Denzel Washington. We headed back to the room. We had a few drinks, packed our bags and went to sleep. On Saturday morning, we packed our bags and discussed the day.

"You have said that you have never traveled with a man. I want to make this weekend special. I want to take you to Kemah. It is not far," William suggested.

We made the thirty-five-minute drive to Kemah. It was not a lot to see on the drive, but I loved the scenery when we arrived. We walked around the boardwalk at Kemah, took pictures and enjoyed the scenery. We located a Mexican restaurant named The Cadillac Bar. We were seated by a window overlooking the water. I excitedly watched as speed boats, sail boats and yachts floated by. I am a sucker for scenery. I ordered the chimichanga with chicken, fried beans and rice. William ordered quesadillas. The food was fresh and good. This was the best Mexican food I had tasted in a long time. The waitress explained the food is made fresh every morning.

I was stuffed. William occasionally opened the door for me. I noticed he did it in front of people. Apparently, he needed praise from others. He needed to feel important. He said his ex-fiancée was a narcissist but so is he. He had an inflated sense of self. Yes sir. Leviathan, you old serpent. What the heck? At least he does not mind driving. So, I'm going to pray for traveling grace and mercy in hopes that we arrive home safely.

While driving back to Fort Worth, William stated that he wanted me to get the full effect of Henderson's chicken. He said he was going to drive by Henderson's once we make it to Dallas. We had to take an alternate route because of a bad car accident. He did not want me to get out of the car. As I think about it, his phone had been blowing up with calls and texts. He only answered for his boys. I'm positive he needed to talk to one of his lady friends and explain his whereabouts for the past four days. I have to give it to him. He is good but not as good as he thinks. He ordered both of us a six piece with fries. We arrived back to Fort Worth safely. I sat at his house and ate two pieces of chicken and some fries. That chicken was good. I said goodbye and headed home. William is not the type to see if I arrived home safely. He was not going to call or text to see if I made it home. He could care less.

I was confused about William because Brittany had shared William was selfless and had given so much of himself to his ex-finance. She had informed me that he did so much for her. Brittany is usually accurate, and I suppose she was accurate about this as well. However, he is not as selfless with me. Apparently, he catered to his ex and he is trying not to overdo it with me. He does the bare minimum. I suppose he is doing just enough to keep the bait on the hook. When this fish gets tired of playing this unhealthy game, I am going back into the water.

Shortly after I arrived home, he called, and I thought he was checking to see if I arrived home safely. NOPE. He was calling to tell me it was too hot in his house. He wishes he did not turn the air off. He never asked if I was home. After I hung up, I started laughing. He is dumb and so am I. I did not hear from William for seven to ten days after we returned from Galveston and Kemah.

Monica said, "Maybe he does not want to feel like he is crowding you."

"Or maybe he is spreading community penis around and has to make it up to the others." Why did I tickle myself? I know I was right.

"I like William. I like the fact that you are not by yourself. Right now, you need him. Just enjoy whatever it is," she said.

"I just know, this is the oddest behavior. We go from spending quality time together to a disappearing act. This dude is not stable at all."

Monica said, "You are thinking too much about it. Men get scared too. Maybe he is falling for you and has gotten cold feet." I did not respond because I did not agree with her. One day I was reading, and alert popped up.

RedHot1: Hi LovelyLady. I am trying to connect with a mature and beautiful woman. I want someone who is beautiful inside and out. I work hard and play hard. I want someone who I can trust because she can trust me, I am tired of doing life alone.

LovelyLady: Hi RedHot1. I don't know what I am trying to do at this point. I cannot say that I am tired of being alone. I am bored with life. I go to work, church, movies and home. If I may be honest, I don't have a clue what I am doing on these sites. I think I am passing away time and entertaining myself.

RedHot1: I understand. Dating is hard. I am a firefighter. I work crazy hours and it is difficult to date. I would like to meet you. BTW: My real name is David. I am divorced and have three adult daughters.

We chatted for a few weeks before exchanging numbers. David called and said he was in the Philippines visiting his brother. His brother moved to the Philippines and married a beautiful woman. They are doing well.

"I am going to be back in Texas in a few days. I would like to take you out for dinner."

"Okay, that will be fine. We can figure out a place to meet."

"I showed my brother your picture and he said you are pretty for a Black woman."

"What ethnicity is your brother?" I asked.

"He is Black, but he cannot stand Black women," he said.

"I suppose y'all mother and grandmother did a number on him, huh," my fangs were coming out.

"I do not understand Black men who hate Black women, but a Black woman gave birth to his silly behind. He has a right to like who he likes but it is unnecessary to take shots at Black women."

David said, "Whoa, he gave you a compliment."

"I do not want his compliment. He does not love himself."

"We are Native American, White and Black," he felt the need to confess.

"When I look at your picture, all I see is a Negro".

David returned to America and invited me to dinner. I chose Chili's on Hulen Street. I waited until he arrived before exiting my car. David was tall and somewhat attractive. We made introductions and entered the restaurant. The hosted seated us and we sat down. David was a talker too. How come people say men do not talk but I meet ones who talk a lot? They start off talking because that is what we want but they stop talking after they reel you in. Men do talk. They talk when they choose to and to whomever they want. Snap out of this fantasy and pay attention. He was still talking and did not realize I had zoned out. I could have sworn he said he has been married three times.

"Wait, what? Tell me about the three marriages", I said. I was really interested.

"I have been married three times but to one woman twice. I cheated on my first wife. Left her and married the mistress, left the mistress and remarried the wife," he looked sad for a moment.

"I loved my first wife, but I was rotten". He said, "She is the only woman I ever loved but I could not be faithful. I messed up. I could not be faithful. It was too many women and too little time. I messed that up. She is remarried and is happy. What is your story?"

"In a nutshell, I meet whores and liars, liars and whores, lazy, liars and whores, whores who are lazy and liars with the exception of Ray." David laughed so hard.

"Has dating really been that bad for you?" He asked.

"It really has been bad. I am not making this up. Ray was the only guy I dated who walked in integrity," I sighed. "So, tell me about the most recent guy," he asked.

"Umm, I met him on this same site. We are not doing well. We are off and on, on and off. He pretends to be a good man but is narcissistic. He is 57 years old and has never been married and does not have any children. It is not going anywhere. He has disappeared. He will resurface. I will entertain him and after I reach my six months I am done," I said with satisfaction.

"He has commitment issues. A man his age who has never been married has no loyalty to anyone other than himself. Coming from a man he is a major whore. It takes one to know one and I know he is not faithful. He is laid up with someone right now feeding her the same lies he is feeding you. At least you know he isn't shit. Excuse my language," David said.

"It's okay," I replied. "Why six months?" "The longest relationship I have ever been in was five years and that was probably six months, but it dragged on for five years. Every time

I meet a guy, it usually ends by the third month. I am trying to see what happens at six months or by the sixth month. Weird, huh? It is my fantasy, and I am living it." Both of us laughed.

"Why didn't you and Ray make it?" He asked.

"I moved to Mississippi. He was not going to leave his mother. Currently, he does not have any children and I would not have any more children if someone offered me a billion dollars," I stuck my tongue out as to see this decision is final. He laughed.

"So, you do not like children?"

"I love children but mine are grown. It is difficult to find a babysitter. Plus, I do not want to get up and feed anyone in the middle of the night. I love my grand babies. I will feed them, but I will not give birth, adopt, foster or try to raise a child of my own. That ship has sailed."

David laughed. "You are funny and easy to talk to."

We ordered our food. I order the same thing every time I go to Chili's. I order the triple dipper which consists of honey chipotle crispers, hot wings, southwestern egg rolls, fried and a margarita. David ordered some wings, broccoli and lemonade. We talked and laughed. David shared that he has been in many fights over women. He has been shot at for sleeping with other folks' women. Most of the turmoil has been due to chasing and sexing women.

"You have three daughters so how would you feel if a man treats them the way you treat women?"

He said, "I have taught my daughters what to look for in a whorish man. They are sharp. Plus, I will kill a man dead if he mistreats my daughters."

"You men people are really weird," I was thinking it but said it out loud.

He said, "I agree".

We both laughed. We finished our food and talked. He messed around and told me that he has two dogs and that he was staying with one of his daughters. My facial expression must have changed.

"I can afford my own place. I am looking for a place to live right now. I cannot decide if I want to buy or build a house. If you want to come over, my daughter wouldn't mind. She is a police officer and can handle you".

"I'm not worried about your daughter, I do not like dogs".

"You do not like dogs or children."

"I love children but do not want any more. I do not like dogs. Can you dig it?"

"I can dig it," he responded with a laugh. I recognized that I get bored easily. I'm ready to go. I thanked him for dinner. He paid and left the tip. I usually leave the tip if a man pays for the meal. We left the restaurant.

He asked me to walk over to his truck because he wanted to show me something. He showed me a Super Bowl ring. He'd played in the NFL for several years and was a part of a championship team. He was watching me as I studied the ring.

"Like I said, I can afford to move out of my daughter's house. I'm not a broke nigga. I would love to see you again."

"I am not concerned about your money or this ring. Money has never impressed me. That is your money. You could be stingy so do not offend me by trying to reel me in with money.

"My bad, Queen. Most women are turned on by money." Blank stare. "I digress. What do you like to do?" He asked.

"I love reading, listening to live bands and my all-time favorite is going to the movies," I sighed. I am so tired of repeating the same things over and over again. Same conversation. I sound like a broken record.

“Let’s go to the movies Sunday afternoon and then dinner.”

“It will have to be after church”.

“You look like a church girl. Let’s eat and then go to the movies or we can go to the Movie Tavern and eat while watching a movie”

“Cool. I get out of church by 1pm. I will go home and change clothes so we can catch a movie around 3pm.”

He walked me to my car and asked for a hug. I tried to give him a church hug. You know the one arm hug where your body language is screaming stay away from me. At any rate, he tries to give me this big full-frontal bear hug and a kiss. I pushed him away from me. I am not comfortable hugging and kissing a stranger.

He snapped, “We are grown. Your ass too good to give me a hug. What the fuck is wrong with you? I see why you are single, fucking prude.”

I’m thinking you Planet of The Apes Caesar looking beast nostrils wide enough to drive a big rig through with your……don’t say it Lisa. Don’t curse at this man. Don’t do it. I had to talk myself down because my fangs had come out. I was in beast mode. Get into your car and drive home. I hopped in my car and drove home unbothered.

Chapter 12

It was about time for William to resurface. His birthday is in August, and we had tossed around some possible things to do for his birthday. He will be 57. Just like I thought, he called. He talked as if he had not disappeared. I played along. He talked in circles but never landed. He invited me to come over because he had grilled some wings and made me a salad. Just like that, I packed a bag and drove over to his house. We looked at some videos on tubing. It looked fun but judging from the videos it looked like only White people did it. I did not see one person of color in the videos. I'm going to try it but I cannot swim. I made the arrangements for us to go tubing down the San Marcos River. William invited some of his friends and family, but all of them declined. I bought a swim skirt, bikini bottom, tankini and water shoes. The day quickly approached, and we headed to Austin, TX. We stayed in Austin, TX and planned on driving to San Marcos the following day. After checking into the hotel, we had to find a Walmart and Family Dollar. William has to have his grapefruit juice to drink with his Vodka. We located a Walmart, put the address in the GPS and headed out. I've heard about Austin traffic, but I am experiencing it for myself. GPS said Walmart was fifteen minutes away. It took us an hour and a half to get to Walmart. We grabbed a few items and headed back to the hotel. We took a nap and woke up hungry. We googled some places to eat. We went to Wingzup. That place had a good assortment of wings. We went back to the room and played quarters. For those who don't know, quarters is a drinking game which involves players bouncing a quarter off a table in an attempt to have the quarter land in a cup. If the quarter does not go into the cup, you have to take a shot. Needless to say, I had to take four shots. I decided I did not like this game. We talked about my birthday plans. Since I do not have any friends in Fort Worth, my plan is to have my birthday party in Jackson, MS so that my family and friends can celebrate with me. William said he definitely wanted to go because people in Mississippi know how to party. I told him the party would be Saturday, December 1st.

We discussed waking up around 9am and driving to San Marcos. William is slow. It takes him longer than a woman to get dressed. I knew we were not going to get up and on the road at 9am. I woke up at 9am and ate some leftover wings for breakfast. I looked over at William who was still asleep. I shook my head. He is so lazy. He is man child. I can't be mad at him because I am enabling him at this point. This weekend had more to do with me than him. He thinks he is pimping me, but I need every break I can get. He finally woke up after I snatched the covers off of him. He got up, got dressed and we headed out. William said he was hungry. We stopped at Whataburger. He got a chicken sandwich. We sat in the car while he ate. He realized that he forgot his swim trunk s and we had to go back to the room in order to get those. He had to make himself a vodka and grapefruit juice before we left. We arrived in San Marcos around 1pm. I was excited to see some people of color going out there as well. We parked the car I went into the bathroom in order to change into my swim attire and we walked down to the counter in order to pay and catch the bus. William was concerned about my safety because I cannot swim. He made sure I was given a life vest. It was the last adult vest. Thank God. We rode these hot buses down to the river. The driver unloaded the tubes. We watched others get onto the tube and into the water. There was a group of five people beside us. They were tying their tubes together.

William asked, "Why are you tying your tubes together?"

A young lady answered, "You may get separated from each other and it is safer that way."

William did not want to tie his tube to mine. The young lady gave me a piece of the string and said, "You won't be sorry. Tie the tubes." I wanted to tie my tube to theirs. He ended up tying our tubes together. We watched the others jump on and now it is our turn. I jumped onto that tube like a pro. That water was cold. We began moving slowly. William noticed that people had beer and snacks. He said, "I wish that I had brought my cooler. I could have brought some beer, drinks for you and some snacks." I just looked at him. Before the trip, I told him that people rented a third tube for snacks and drinks, but he did not listen. He thinks he knows everything. He began asking different people for beer. He was not afraid to beg. At that moment, I was thinking he is a total bum. It was fun floating down the lazy river. Everyone was nice and friendly. People did not hesitate to give him a beer whenever he asked. He cannot seem to do anything without drinking beer or Vodka.

The entire floating experienced lasted for two and a half hours. We ended up behind the building where we purchased the tubes. I went to the bathroom, dried off and changed clothes. I did not know they had showers. I did not bring any body wash. Well, I am dry enough and will have to shower as soon as I get back to the hotel. William asked me to take a few pictures of him. There background was beautiful. He asked for the keys, but I declined. "I do not want you to drive after you have been drinking," I said. "You don't trust your man. I am a beast. I can drink and drive," he said with that cocky attitude.

"You can drink and drive with one beer but several… I cannot trust you to drive. You drank six or seven beers. I am driving. You can play with your life, but I want to live."

He looked as though he wanted to argue but he hopped in the passenger seat.

We headed back to Austin. We stopped at the gas station. William filled the tank and bought us food from Long John Silver. He was in a good mood. It was amazing how much fun we had whenever we went out of town. It always felt right whenever we went out of town not so much in Fort Worth. We went back to the room, showered and looked for food. I wanted to try Pluckers Wing Bar. We drove up and down 6th street in search of food. I love the culture on 6th street. It was people everywhere. I like the atmosphere of Austin. Pluckers was so packed. Every restaurant we went to was packed. We drove around some more and decided to go back to Wingzup. We decided to dine in. I ordered wings, waffle fries and margaritas. We ate laughed and talked. We went back to the room. We packed our bags and went to bed. He played on his phone while I watched television. Every now and again, he would show me a video on Facebook. I know he was nervous that a text or phone call would pop up on the screen.

On Sunday morning, we headed back to Fort Worth. There are periods whereas William was engaging. He would talk and talk. There are times he was a million miles away. I know he is planning to disappear. I am very familiar with his behavior and pattern now. He will act like he does not want to be bothered with me, I will give him space, he will resurface in a few weeks as if nothing happened. Until I get tired, I will entertain this mess. I wonder why it is so easy for men to meet someone, but it is difficult for women to meet someone else? I was not trying to be faithful to William. I just could not meet anyone. We arrived safely back to Fort Worth. I dropped him off and did not look back.

I knew it would be 7 to 10 days before he resurfaced. I met Peter through an acquaintance. Peter worked for the post office. He was divorced and a single father. He was raising fraternal twins ages 17 years old. We talked or shall is say Peter talked. Peter was a talker. I looked up to heaven and asked, God, am I on candid camera? God, Jesus, Joseph, Moses, Paul, Mary, Luke, Abraham, Gabriel and Michael must be laughing at me. I wonder if other women are going through this. Peter talked and talked. I danced for thirty minutes, and he was still talking. I began to journal. He was still talking. I curled my hair. He was still talking. He did not stop talking. I finally interrupted and said, "I have to go. It was nice listening to you." I looked at my phone and he had talked for one hour and 46 minutes. Peter invited me to meet him at Mercado Juarez in The Highlands. We agreed to meet at 12:45pm. Peter was late. I sat in the car talking to Gwen until he arrived. He told me he drove a Cadillac and I knew it was him driving fast in the parking lot. He waved. I snapped a picture of his car and him as he exited the vehicle. We shook hands. Peter was 6'3'' but walked like a man who was 99. I was not attracted to him at all. He was a decent looking fella, but I can tell he was raised by an old person. He had on church shoes, jeans, and a polo shirt. He was dressed like somebody's granddaddy.

I said, "You are 50yearsold, right?"

He replied, "Yes, I look younger, don't I?"

I was thinking no but I did not respond. We entered the restaurant and waited to be seated. We were escorted to a table in nice spot. The waitress handed us our menus and Peter began complaining about the prices. The food was inexpensive. I rolled my eyes. I do not care about prices if I am hungry.

"I can pay for my own food, or I can leave. It does not really matter to me," I said.

Peter, "It is not expensive, but I like to get my money's worth. You know these restaurants don't give you what they charge."

Peter began talking about being off work due to an injury. He'd injured his leg at work and is trying to get disability.

"I am tired of working," he said.

I came to the conclusion that Peter is broke too. He owned his home and he shared it with his children. Both children will graduate next year. He will be an empty nester. Peter talked non-stop. Peter's wife cheated with the neighbor and married him. His children wanted to stay with him. They visit their mother who lives on the next block.

"I was hurt at first, but they sold the house and moved into a house one block over," Peter explained. "I work nights I suppose she got lonely. I can't blame her for moving on. It has been five years and I have dated but nothing works out especially since I work at night. Maybe it will work out for us. You seem like an understanding woman. My friend told me she thinks we will be good together. My friend is very successful. I promote her business. She told me the two of you met at a function. I love going to different functions. I love attending Black functions. I love to cook. My momma taught me how to cook. I can cook anything. I can cook better than a woman. Shoot, the last woman I dated still asks me to cook her certain meals. I don't have this gut for nothing. My children love my cooking. I should open a restaurant. I can cook any types of food. My children are honor roll students. I was smart like that when I was in school. Did I tell you I was born and raised on the south side of Chicago? Did I tell you I graduated from Whitney Young? Have you ever been to Chicago? We moved to Arkansas and then Texas. My mother and sister went back to Chicago. I stayed in Texas because I met and married my wife. I try to go back and visit as much as I can. I have not been back in a long time. I am going home this year. I am a mommy's boy. My mommy would like you. She loves pretty women. She will be like Peter found him a pretty girl."

As he continued to talk, I was mentally punching him in the face and that made me smile. I began looking around. *Where is the waitress?* Finally, the waitress came over. I had no intention of drinking, but I need a margarita. I ordered a grand margarita. I told Peter I would pay for my drink since he was worried about prices. The waitress returned with our drinks. Peter asked for water. We placed our order and Peter resumed talking. "Man, tell me about yourself. Why are you single? How many children do you have? You have children, right? Where do you work? Did you go to college?"

"I didn't graduate but I started. I keep saying I am going to go back to college. I have not found the time. My children are going to college. Both of them will get academic scholarships. Both want to be engineers. Both are talented. Both of them can sing. They can be anything they want. I am proud of them. We are really close. They want me to meet someone. They said I need to get out more. I do need to get out more".

The more he talked, the more I drank. When the waitress returned with our food, I asked for another margarita. Peter talked while we ate. I was not able to respond to any of his questions. While he talked, I took pleasure in my food and margaritas. After we finished eating, he continued talking. He finally stopped talking and said, "You're really quiet."

"No, I am not quiet. You are really talkative," I said

Peter laughed and said, "Girl, you are so crazy."

"No. Peter you are," I said with a hint of sarcasm. Peter wanted me to know that he was broke too. He said his ex-wife took all of his money.

Let's see, William and Peter are broke financially, both own their own homes, and both are lazy. William does not want a "real" job because he does not want anyone to tell him what to do. Peter is tired of working and trying to get disability. I am definitely on candid camera. Someone is laughing at me. Black men used to be the hardest working group of men. What happened? My granddaddy worked until his leg was amputated. Some of these modern-day men want maximum results with minimum actions. Will I meet a man with drive and determination? Will I meet one with precision and purpose? Do they exist? They have to. I see them on television, and I hear about them. I just don't meet them. This group of men have turned me off. I don't want to be a lesbian, but I am giving up hope about eligible men. I wonder if most men are like these two and women just suffer in silence.

William disappeared for three weeks this time. He resurfaced mid-September.

"Hey bae. -What have you been up to? -I been missing you. I called you but you never answered your phone," He lied.

"What up Mr. William Antoine aka Disappearing Acts aka Miss Dove" Smith? Who are you bored with this week?"

"Quit playing. You know I'm a good man". I choked. He really believes that lie.

"If you say so, good man."

"My boy told me he saw you on a dating site".

"Who is your boy? I have only met two of your friends?"

"I showed him your picture. He said he talked to you."

"You and your friend are liars, I see. I know who I talk to and when."

"My sister told me I need to get over myself and call you. She said you are a good woman, and I am messing up."

"You can't help that you are silly. It's not your fault. Bless your heart," I said.

"When am I going to see you?"

"I don't feel like playing with you this week," I expressed.

"Don't be like that. My boy is having a party next Saturday and I want you to go. It is a black and white party." William called and texted the entire week.

I called Brittany. "Hey gal, what are you up to?"

"I was calling to give you an update. Sister, I like William but not really. I like him more than Peter and the other ones I have met but William is such a lying wonder. He is so unstable. I wonder if I like him because he is unstable and inconsistent. He is not the best-looking man on the planet. A part of me likes him and a part of me pities him. He is wounded and broken. Maybe I am attracted to the broken part of him."

Brittany began praying. Afterwards, she said, "I hear the spirit of the Lord saying. He loves you but he does not know how to show it. He really loved that last woman, and she broke him. He wants to love again but is afraid. He enjoys you but it scares him. Deep down he is a good guy but he is hurting. He keeps chasing behind these Jezebel type women. He has given in to his flesh. He feels bad because he cannot take care of you. He feels inadequate because he is broke. He knows you do not need him financially and that bothers him. I believe he is going to ask you to marry him around Christmas time."

"Okay, thanks lady. Have a good evening," I said. I was incredulous about this prophetic word.

I called Monica and told her that William had invited me to his friend's birthday party. "See, I told you to be patient with him. He has to like you because he is taking you out and you are meeting friends."

"That does not mean anything to a man. Meeting friends and family used to solidify relationships but now none of this means anything. It just means we are going to a party."

"I will let you know how it goes."

"Have fun and take plenty of pictures."

William called Saturday morning in order to see if we were still on for tonight. I said, "I will be there. I will meet you at your house around 7ish."

He said, "The party does not start until 8pm and you know our people won't be on time."

"I like to be on time so I will see you later."

I arrived at William's house around 7:15pm. I knew I looked cute, but he is not generous with compliments. His closest thing to a compliment was asking where is my shawl?

I spoke with Bonnie. She asked if William liked what he saw.

"Honey, he is not one that compliments."

"I know you look cute," she said.

"Thanks, hun. I reckon I will get ready to go. You can tell a lot about a person by his friends. I will let you know how it goes."

We arrived at 8:15pm and not a lot of people had arrived.

"I told you people would be late. The birthday boy isn't here yet."

"Lord, we just can't be on time, can we?" It was rhetorical. I laughed. I sat at a table close to the bathroom and exit. Every room I enter, I have an exit strategy and I have to pee a lot. This table works for me. William walked around talking to a few people. More and more people started to show up around 9 pm. William's childhood friend entered and sat at the table with us. William said." Junior this is my baby, Lisa." We hugged.

Junior said, "William knows how to treat a woman until he gets on that shit. Once he gets on that shit……he gets stupid."

William froze. He sat like a deer caught in head lights. I suppose "on that shit" means once he starts messing with other women. I wanted to say that has already started but I am quite sure Junior knew that already. William introduced me as bae to some and Lisa to others. I was paying attention to how he introduced me and to whom.

I turned to him and said, "Steve Harvey said pay attention to the way a man introduces you. He will tell you what he thinks of you and what position you are in by the way he introduces you."

Another childhood friend entered the building, he introduced me to her as his girlfriend. I said, "Nice to meet you, I am Lisa."

Because I had time for it, I turned to him, "You introduced me as your girlfriend because I brought it to your attention."

"I don't know what I am going to do with you."

"You aren't going to do anything with me. You don't know what to do with yourself." He laughed.

The party was BYOB. I had purchased a bottle of Jack Daniel's Tennessee honey. I drank it with Sprite. Bonnie had showed me how to mix it. I'm still not good at it. I always pour more liquor than Sprite. I was actually having a good time. I'm actually getting out and meeting new people. It's a shame. I didn't know a single person in the room. I didn't feel uncomfortable. Everyone made me feel welcome. I started reflecting on how alone I am. I am in a room full of strangers with the exception of William. I see why people commit suicide. Isolation can drive you mad. As I watch William and his friends interact with each other, I have never felt more alone. My life is pitiful. I have had no success in life or love. Why did I just burst out laughing? I believe it will get greater later. The words of Bishop T. D. Jakes resonated, "*Someone can take your hand and win.*" It does not look good right now, but I am going to keep living and keep pressing.

I began fantasizing about Ray. I was wondering if we would have still been together had I never left Chicago. Why did I date and marry my children's father? Why didn't I join a convent and be a nun like I originally planned? I'm not Catholic but a nun's life looked appealing and free of heartbreak. I am non denominational nun now. Cause ain't nun going on in my life. Did you get my joke? Nun going on in my life. I crack myself up.

My fantasy ended. I came back down to earth and there was William. He had drunk half of his Vodka. I only had two drinks because I know I will have to be the designated driver. William is a recovering alcoholic or border line alcoholic. Since I was not drinking my liquor, William's friend Junior asked if he could taste it. He drank one cup, two cups, three cups etc. I suppose free liquor tastes better.

William asked, "Why aren't you drinking? I want you to have fun?"

"I am having fun. I don't need to get drunk to have a good time. I am good."

"You are worried about us getting home safely. I am not going to let nothing happen to you. I can get us home".

"No worries. Drink your little heart out. I am getting home safely." One of William's cousins entered the party. Shortly afterwards, his cousin's girlfriend entered the party. William introduced me to them. I noticed that his cousin's girlfriend was cold towards William. I immediately knew there was some bad blood between them. They had a taco bar which was delicious. I actually was having a good time. The party was lit as the young people would say. Junior's fiancé came to the party and sat at the table with us. Junior introduced me to Brandy. We made plans to go on double dates. I went from table to table talking to different people. A group of men went outside. A group women danced. We went back to the table and the men came back into the building. Junior poured another cup of Tennessee Whiskey. I look over at him and noticed he was asleep. I told William to check on his friend. William got up and shook Junior. Junior fell out of his chair and onto the floor. Someone yelled call 911. Someone else poured cold water on him. Brandy was crying. People began standing over him.

One guy said, "He needs to lose weight."

Someone else said, "He has sleep apnea." I pushed my chair against the wall, grabbed my purse and sat in that chair like Ms. Celie in Harpo's Juke Joint. Sho Nuff. I had not seen this level of foolery in a very long time.

Junior wasn't dead. He was breathing. William was right there in the thick of it trying to help his friend. He was very attentive towards his friend. That was endearing. I supposed no one ever called for help because the paramedics did not show. Someone turned on the lights and said the party is over. I looked to my left and a woman fell out of her chair. She was drunk too. I didn't know whether to laugh or cry so I laughed. Someone told Brandy to get Junior home. William asked if I would follow them home because he was going to drive Junior's car home. I kept asking for their address in order to put it in the GPS. Everyone was emotionally charged but no one answered. I cannot stand this level of chaos and confusion. I ended up following Junior and Brandy to their apartment. Once we arrived at their apartment, Brandy thanked me for following them.

She asked, “Where is William? I thought he was following us.”

“I thought so too.”

“Do you want me to wait outside with you?”

“No. I am fine.” I called William but he did not answer his phone. I called multiple times and no answer. William finally calls and says, “Bae, I am at a friend’s house in Meadowbrook. Will you pick me up from here?

In agitation I say, “What the hell? Your raggedy behind tells me to follow them but you are on the other side of town?”

William said, “I don’t know where they live. They moved into a new apartment.”

Under my breath I said, “Dumb ass.” I asked, “How come you did not get the address and put it into your GPS?” Lisa, do you really want to be bothered with a drunk? This is what your life will be like. Clearly, William is a borderline or recovering alcoholic. You have to want more for yourself than this.

I drove to Meadowbrook in order to pick William up. When I walked up to the door, William and Benny were talking loudly. I was ringing the doorbell, knocking and calling William’s phone. I had to take a deep breath. It is freaking 3 o’clock in the morning. Out of frustration, I laid on that doorbell. Benny finally realized that someone was ringing the doorbell and lets me in. I am in stupid mode at this point.

“Dude, it is time to go.” Benny offered me a beer.

“No thanks. I am ready to go.”

William continued with that loud drunken voice, “Man, we need to get together. Bae, this man throws some good parties. We are going to have to come over here one day.”

“Sure. You can but I’m not. Let’s go. It was nice meeting you.” William said, “You are mean.”

“You are drunk,” I shot back.

All the way to his house, William talked about the past. How much fun he used to have? How much money he used to have; I felt sorry for him because he is stuck in the past. His entire focus is on his past life. I could not wait to get in the bed and go to sleep. I am so tired of listening to him talk about the person he “used to be”.

I went to sleep because I was tired, and I needed to go to church. Needless to say, I overslept. I jumped up without taking a shower, packed my bags and went home. I was aggravated with William and did not want to hear his voice or be around him while he nursed a hangover. At this moment, I was disgusted with him. I was disgusted with myself.

Chapter 13

We were off and on again so many times. September is football season. According to William, he loves football. He asked for Sundays as a time to watch football. He loves the New Orleans Saints. He stated that he is a part of this group that watches the games at Buffalo Wild Wings. I am a Cleveland Browns fan, so I did not want any part of that. William invited me to come watch the game but only if I wore Saints, attire.

"Honey, I have my own identity and know which team I like. I am not wearing any Saints gear."

"If you are going to be with me you have to become a Saints fan," he said.

"Ninja, you sound like a foolish person."

William is passionate about the Saints and Drew Brees. I secretly love the Saints too. I would not dare tell him that, but I am not going to wear any Saints gear just because he asked. I feel like he is trying to make me lose my individuality.

Due to William's limited finances, we did not go out much unless I planned it. Trust, he was not lying about his finances. This ninja was broke. I appreciate the fact that he cooked for me. Where did he get the money for groceries? I'm glad you asked. People sell and buy food stamps all the time. Although I appreciated home cooked meals, I have grown accustomed to dining out several times per week. I was getting antsy going from his house to my apartment. I wanted to go out to eat. I knew just the place. It has good food, and a live band and a DJ. Jamaican Gates has authentic island food and is located in Arlington, TX. I invited William to join me. I drove by his house in order to pick him up. One of his friend's was there and they had been drinking. At least he was not drunk. He introduced me to his friend. His friend chatted for a few minutes and left. We got dressed and headed to the restaurant. It suddenly began to rain. It was pouring. His driving was off.

"How much did you have to drink?" I asked.

"I only had two glasses. I knew we were going out and I was not going to overdo it. I did not want to hear your mouth. Don't you trust your man? he asked.

"Not if he has been drinking. I do not trust anyone who does not know their limits."

Upon arrival, William found a parking space by the door because it was pouring down. He dropped me off in front of the restaurant and parked the car. The hosted seated us right near the dance floor. I hate being exposed like this, but all of the other tables were taken. We listened to a band, watched people dance and ordered drinks. William began talking about all of the fun he had in Jamaica. I was wrong but I fed into his stories. I don't believe he has done half of the things he bragged about. He has an inflated sense of self. I believe he has delusions of grandeur. He may have been to Jamaica, but he lies so much until I have a hard time believing anything he says. Every time he opens his mouth, he is lying about something. I looked at him and smiled. I was thinking he is probably broke because he has done so much in the past which means he has poor money management skills. The waitress came and took our order. I ordered the jerk chicken with rice and peas. William ordered oxtails, cabbage with macaroni and cheese. This old man paid for our drinks. William had beer after beer. He was good and drunk by 10:30pm. It was getting late, and I wanted to leave so I could prepare and rest before church tomorrow.

The waitress brought the bill and sat it next to me. Either she knows him or it shows that he is broke. I told him he has to pay for all of his alcoholic beverages. I would pay for the food. I encouraged him to leave a tip too. It had stopped raining. As we were walking to the car, five beautiful sisters were walking into the restaurant. William could not get in the car. Honey, he stood there so the women could look at him. I was mentally screaming *please look at him. Someone please validate this man.* When he finally got into the car, I was staring at him.

"What?" he asked.

"You are so pitiful, just pitiful," I said laughing. "You really need attention from every woman you see. Your identity and self-esteem are based upon a woman looking at you. Do you feel like you are that fine whereas women are falling at your feet? Bless your heart." He became defensive. "What did I do? I did not do anything? Stop being so jealous."

"Dear, I am not jealous. I actually feel sorry for you". There I had said it out loud. I actually did feel sorry for him.

I do not like to bad mouth people, but he is pathetic and so am I for dealing with him. Brittany and Monica see the good in William. I see some good qualities, but he is not, yet the man God has revealed to them. Prophetically, God must have shown them the man he used to be or that he will become. Because he has not yet arrived, he gave the good part of who he is to his ex. He probably didn't give her his good part either or she would still be with him. Dang grief.... I need to heal. I'm dealing with crap I would not deal with under normal circumstances. I'm hanging on because I am grief stricken, confused, lonely and bored. He is filling some space and killing some time.

A few weeks had gone by and we were off not on. I had left some of my case files in a cabinet at his house. I called and asked him to drop them off or meet me somewhere. He asked me to come and get them.

"I am not doing anything. You can come and get them. I do not touch your work stuff."

"I will be there in thirty minutes or less."

The door was unlocked as usual. I entered.

"What up sucka? What you know good?"

"Nothing, just chilling. Work has been steady."

"I did not come to tarry. I just need my papers."

Upon entering the dining room, William had a picture of an attractive young lady on his stand. She was standing next to an older gentleman. "Who is this person? She is cute" I asked.

"That is my niece," he responded quickly. I have never heard William talk about a niece. He lied so quickly and kept talking. He used to have my card in the same spot. I chuckle. I'm quite sure he forgot to take it down. He presents himself to be such a good man and the last thing he wants to do is get caught up in his own lies.

Remember, you are trying to break your three-month cycle. I have to give myself a pep talk. You can do this. You have to make it to December with William. Just overlook his whorish and lying ways. You are not having sex with him, so you don't have to worry about catching a sexually transmitted disease. I was smiling all the while thinking, he really thinks I believe him. I grabbed my papers and left.

September was a blur. He reached out and invited me to his brother's wedding.

I called Monica, "William invited me to his brother's wedding, but I am having reservations."

Monica said, "It sounds like y'all are a real couple. A man doesn't just take any woman to his brother's wedding. Go and have fun."

I decided to go to the wedding and reception. I met a lot of his family that night. They were not extremely friendly. They were not rude. Call me paranoid but I had this gut feeling that they felt sorry for me because they knew I was one of many. Family knows us best. I suppose they knew I would not last long and there was no point getting attached to me. Nevertheless, I had a good time. Everything was pretty. I enjoyed myself and the food was great.

Williams' ex-girlfriend and the bride were friends. He made a point to introduce me to her as his girlfriend. I knew he wanted the bride to tell his ex-girlfriend that he brought a date to the wedding. And folks say men aren't messy. He wanted to take pictures, but I declined. He has never wanted to take pictures with me. This was for show, and I was not partaking in it. He knew those pictures would be posted all over Facebook and his ex would definitely see them. William wanted to send a message that he was happy and has moved on. Dude, you are not happy with yourself let alone with me. After the reception, we went our separate ways yet again.

William reached out and asked me to come over the first week of October. He had a way of reeling me back in with his words, no actions just words. We were not sexually active. At least I wasn't, I saw the KY Jelly when he opened his nightstand. He claimed he uses it to masturbate. I shrugged not because I believed him but because I am not having sex with him. Believe it or not, I spent plenty of nights at his house and he spent plenty of nights at mine. Believe you me there was no sex between us.

I spent four days at William's house. On the third day, he began having nightmares. He would fight in his sleep and kick me, but I would always kick him back. I know those demons were fighting him in his sleep, but I am fighting him and the demons. I kicked him as hard as I could. He would wake up.

"What is wrong with you?" He asked.

"You are having one of those nightmares. But you are probably doing it on purpose because you want me to go home."

"You know I have nightmares. Something or someone is always chasing me in my dreams." He shared.

"Yes, it is the demons you have invited you're your life."

On the fourth day, I had an event at work. It was a work retreat where all of us get together, play games and eat. We had to dress and perform to a song from the 90s. We chose Girls Just Want to

Have Fun by Cyndi Lauper. I got up, got dressed and headed to Burleson, TX. I returned to William's house around 3pm. I talked about how much fun we had. It began raining really hard. We ordered wings from Pizza Hut. William went from engaging to distant. Earlier that week, he had asked me to move in and marry him. Now he is sitting his ugly self over there acting like he does not want to be bothered. I'm tired of him and his mood swings.

This dude is bipolar or Narcissistic or both. I sat staring at him. From May to July and part of August, he love bombed me. August to October, he is in the discarding phase of the situationship. I believe he was discarding me in June too. I just wasn't paying attention. I ate my food and packed my belongings.

"Wait, what are you doing? You don't have to leave. Don't take all of your stuff. I am not asking you to leave".

"Oh, but I do have to leave. You have not verbally asked me to leave but your actions are saying go. I'll take actions for $200 Alec."

He carried my bags to the car and asked me to stay. I waved and drove off. I was not thinking. I should have packed all of my stuff. I just wanted to go home.

I did not reach out to him, nor did he reach out to me. In mid October, I had grown really tired of the foolishness. I was working late, and I thought about my Marc Jacobs Daisy perfume that I left at his house along with my Fenty beauty products, Soft Soap body wash, Sephora brushes, moisturizer, soap, pajamas, slippers, toothpaste, dresses, shoes, curling irons, vaginal wash and deodorant. I specifically left a half bottle of Orange Blossom wash in the shower. I do not think it was fair that someone else gets to use my products. I called and asked for him to pack my stuff and I will come and get it.

After two weeks of asking, he said, "No one is going to bother your stuff. I will give it back when I get ready."

That pissed me off. On this particular night in October, he called like we had been talking consistently, “Hey, how are you doing?”

I could tell he was driving. “I’m on my way to do a job”.

I said, “A hand job. Hey, I want my stuff tonight.” As quickly as he called, he hung up.

I called back but he did not answer. I left a voicemail saying that I am coming to get my stuff now. I sent a text message and told him to have my stuff packed and I will be there within the hour. William never returned my call or texts. Upon arrival, his car is in the driveway and a there is a Black SUV in front of the house as well. His light is on in the dining room. I knocked on the door and waited for a response. No answer. I called. No answer. I texted. No response.

“William. I want my stuff. I am not here to cause problems. I just want my stuff and to cut my losses. If you are home just pack up my belongings and sit them outside the door. Ma’am, if you are in there. You can pack up my stuff. I don’t fight women over men. I just want my stuff. I bought it and I want it.”

No response. I went to the side door and knocked. “William, I’m sorry if you are having sex. Get up and pack my stuff. I will leave. I just want my stuff. Do not worry, Miss. I am not violent. I don’t scratch cars or cut tires. I just want what belongs to me.”

I called Bonnie who did not answer. I called Monica and told her that I was at William’s house, and I wanted my stuff.

“Monica, I want my stuff, but he is not answering.”

“Why are you at that man’s house?” She asked.

“I told him I was on my way. He has allowed me to come to his house announced since we have been “dating,” I replied. I knocked again. Monica directed me to leave.

“Get in the car before he calls the police.”

Everyone knows I do not fool with the police or jail. I realized I was acting like Taraji P. Henson in Acrimony. I had snapped. I wanted my stuff. I high tailed it from his neighborhood. William finally called thirty minutes later.

"What is wrong? I see all of these missed calls from you."

"I called and told you I was coming to get my stuff. I did not realize you were as cruel as you are."

"See you got it all wrong," he said.

"You are sorry dude. I just want my stuff." I hung up on him. I burst out laughing fifteen minutes later. I laughed because of what was I thinking. *His no teeth, no job, lazy and broke assets was not worth the time I spent with him. I just want my stuff.*

Monica called. "I'm going to need you not to leave anything at a man's house again."

"Heck, that was the first and last time. I would not have given him that many chances had I not listened to you and Brittany. I knew this ninja wasn't worth a damn. I knew he was garbage but you two kept saying he sounds nice and give him a chance. I am NEVER wrong about a man. I'm pissed off at myself more so than him. He is who he is. I am the one out of character. That broke bitch. He has probably used all of my products."

Monica said, "You have too much to lose. You don't need to be bothered with that. I have never known you to act this way."

"I have never left my stuff at a man's house either. I can assure you that won't happen again," I said.

I laughed in spite of. I made it home, put on pajamas and went to sleep. A few days later, William called. "I cannot believe a professional woman like you were over here acting like that. My neighbor told me that you were yelling. I don't need that type of drama around here."

"I apologize for acting out of character, but I told you I wanted my stuff."

"I was not at home. I was hanging televisions with my brother." I rolled my eyes. He was hanging his penis in someone else's vagina. If he felt the need to lie, go for it.

I will give him a break. The first time we broke up, I missed him. Now, I definitely didn't miss him. I was still trying to date but no success. I had talked to a couple of guys but no dates. I'd started having a lot of dreams about William. I dreamt about him under some sort of emotional attack. In almost every dream he was cornered by a very strong woman. The woman would look at me and say you can't have him. In every dream it was a different woman, and he would be sitting in a chair unable to talk. It was as if each woman had him in a trance. I began to pray for him. I unblocked his number the week before Thanksgiving in order to see how he was doing.

"Hi, I am just checking about you. You were on my mind." "I've been calling you, but I know my number is blocked."

"Yes sir. You didn't want anything. Plus, you were embarrassed because of the ruckus I made at your house in October. We know your image is everything to you," I said.

William said, "I can't believe you did that."

"Well, if you had answered your phone, you would have known I wanted my stuff, but you were being evil," I said through laughter. "Oh, it's funny huh?"

"Absolutely, I should have never done that. All it did was make me appear to be crazy in love or crazy, but it had nothing to do with you." It is my stuff. I paid for it, and you were holding it hostage. I want my stuff.

"I will give it to you when I get ready," he said. "You controlling, warlock," I spat. "I miss you," he said. "I don't miss you not as a man friend. I miss the thought of having a man and some company, but that drama you are offering is not what I want in life."

In his typical fashion, he deflects. "What are you doing for Thanksgiving" he asked.

"I am cooking for me and my children".

"Can I come over? I can help you cook."

"Sure. Please don't try anything slick. Your nasty behind been slinging penis around the DFW area. You know you think you are the answer to every woman's prayer."

"I know you don't like to cook so what are you cooking?" He asked.

I said, "Turkey, dressing, mac and cheese, deviled eggs, baked beans, candied yams, cabbage, honey ham and yeast rolls".

"I have to see that for myself."

"Well, you can come over next Wednesday in order to help me cook," I said. We did not talk until the following week.

The week of Thanksgiving arrived quickly. Thanksgiving is one of my favorite holidays. It reminds me of growing up in the Mississippi Delta with my maternal family members. Those were the best of times. Oh, how I long for those days but I can never get them back. Thanksgiving is a pagan holiday, but it is a good time to be lazy and spend with your loved ones. I stop daydreaming and get back to present day. We are always granted special leave the Wednesday before Thanksgiving. I was looking forward to getting off at noon on Wednesday. Last year, I was supposed to get off at noon but there was a lot of drama with a family. I was not able to get off early. I had a feeling I was not going to get off early this year either. I did not speak it out loud, but I had that gut feeling.

I was sitting at my desk wrapping up a case. It is 11:30am. I hope I can make it. It's almost noon. My phone rang and it was my supervisor. Rylee said, "I am sorry, but I placed a case on your workload."

My heart sank. She continued, "All you have to do is call and schedule a time to meet with the family".

Before dialing the number, I knew it would not be that simple. It is never that simple for me. To make a long story short, it was not as simple as a phone call. It was family unnecessary family drama. I was pissed. I told the family that it is Thanksgiving Eve. This is supposed to be a time for family, but you all are acting a fool and for what. Needless to say, I had to drive an unruly teenager two and a half hours one way. I spent five hours round trip. I called William and told him I would not be home until midnight. William said he was coming over no matter how late it is.

William came over around 11:45pm. I was in the process of putting case notes in the system. We laughed and talked. We peeled the potatoes, boiled the eggs, and prepped the turkey. While cooking the ground beef, I stared at him while he was talking. He began telling me how to cook the ground beef. I silently thought. *He is really a know it all. I don't know what I saw in him. He should have been a homeboy. I suppose it is true that we date our assignments.*

I woke up early on Thanksgiving and finished cooking dinner. My children came over. All of us had a good time. William said, "I'm getting ready to go to my nephew's house."

It was 6:30ish when I walked him to his car. "So, you were not going to invite me, huh?"

He said, "Weren't you at my house acting up?"

"Oh dear, you are going to keep using that excuse," I said.

"You know I don't want to go, right? You do know that I am up on your game. Why do you think I don't have sex with you? I know you are going to someone else's house and do dinner with her and her family. That is where you will get your sex. I really just want your company." I waved and walked away smiling. Upon entering the apartment, my children said that dude talks to much. He is cool but he would not shut up. I explained he needs everyone's approval so his way of getting people to like him is for him to appear intelligent and knowledgeable. He needs the approval of everyone in the room. My children said all of that talking would get on their nerves. I had to laugh because William enjoyed talking to everyone except me. My children went up at 10pm.

I turned on some praise and worship music and cleaned up. I had a good night's sleep. I was up the next day because we were on call. That is the thing about Social Services. We spend more time caring for other people while neglecting our own homes. I did not expect to hear from William anymore. He actually called the following morning. He verbalized having a good time at his nephew's house. He "got drunk". His entire family was there. He spent the night at his nephew's house and came home this morning. My other line rang. I told William I had to take this call.

Monica called, "How was your Thanksgiving?"

"It was good". I decided not to tell her William had come over because she would be hopeful. Monica and Brittany are two of the reasons I talked to him for as long as I did.

Monica always defended him. We actually had a dispute over her constantly defending him. I had told Monica that I can be his friend but not his lady. William said he did not want to be my friend. Monica said, "I would not want to be your friend either the way you acted at his house."

"It was a onetime incident and not the end of the world. Why are you always defending him? I know why? You have been waiting on your man for ten years, so I see why you don't see anything wrong with the way William has treated me".

Monica said, “You don’t have to be so mean.”

“You snapped first. I apologize for the way I said it but I meant what I said. People give advice based on the type of love they accept or feel they deserve. You have low self-esteem. Apparently, we both do, or we would not accept that type of foolery”.

Monica said, “I am going to hang up before we go too far and can’t come back from this.”

Bonnie called, “Are you excited about your party?” “Yes, ma’am I am. I’m more excited about being off work for the next ten days,” I answered.

“What are you wearing? Bonnie asked.

“It’s a secret. Everyone else is wearing black and white. I want everybody to be casual and comfortable.”

“Is William coming?” She asked.

“I have not talked to him since the day after Thanksgiving. Today is the 25th. I will call him after I get off the phone with you. That should give him a chance to lie to whomever.”

Monica called, “I am trying to make it to the party, but I do not think I am going to be able to. Driving from Chicago and having to turn right back around will be too exhausting”.

“It is okay. I understand.”

She asked, “Is William going?”

“We have not talked about it since August. I will call him because I have not had a date on my birthday since 1999. I suppose I will have him accompany me.”

Monica said, “At least invite him to drive and just to have company on the road. At least you can say you had a date on your birthday and don’t think too much about it. He will be more than happy to go.”

I said, “Of course, the trip is free. Food, hotel and gas are at my expense so mooching is his middle name.”

Monica said, “Please don’t say that to him.”

“Cuzzo, you know he is a user.”

She said, “He is a taker.”

I squealed, “What is the difference between a taker and a user? A taker is a person who takes a specified thing. A user is one who uses. He takes but never gives. I’m not understanding. You know you can justify for a man,” I continued, “I’m indecisive because my family is so warm and welcoming. They will get attached to him and start asking what happened to him. You know he is such a charmer. He will act like he likes me in front of them and I do not want to have to answer for his absence.”

Monica said, “Just take him with you. Live your life and don’t talk to him after that and you don’t owe your family any explanations about where he is.”

“Chat with you later, gator.”

We said our goodbyes. After hanging up the phone, I began thinking about my failed relationships. Am I the only woman who goes through this? This man is poison and I know it.

I take a deep breath before scrolling through my contacts and locating his name.

I called and he said, “Oh you are acting funny”.

I said, “No, your thing is not talking on the phone. The way I see it, there is no purpose in calling you”.

As he was talking, I began reminiscing. Here is the deal. William was blowing up my phone when we first met. He responded to text messages too. Three months in, the phone calls became less and less. He began saying, “I don’t like talking on the phone.” For a man who does not like talking on the phone, he talked to his best friend two or three times per day, his nephews and other friends. He did not like talking to me. I came back to earth.

"As you know I am having my birthday party in Mississippi. I would like you to attend."

"I don't know because I don't know what you have told your family about me," he stated.

"Honey, you are not worth that much effort. All my family knows is we are off and on again. I told them you are a whore and a liar, but they will not mistreat you. We have whores and liars in our family, and we accept them too. They won't mistreat you."

"I will think about it," he said.

"Well, you have one week to get your lies together," I said.

"What do you mean get my lies together?" He asked.

"Steve Harvey said if a man is off with you, he is on with someone else. I'm quite sure there are several others. You are not the faithful kind. So, if I'm good enough to be cheated on and lied to. Whoever they are can be lied to. You won't be cheating with me so that part will be okay."

During the course of the week, William's grown behind would text that dreadful 'wyd'. This is a 57-year-old man. He finally asked what the dates are. I provided the dates and said just tell them it is a work trip. Technically, you are my driver.

The following Friday, I pulled up in front of his house.

He said, "Come inside. I got you something for your birthday."

I entered the home and there was a big bag on the table. I was nervous because most guys I have dated do not know my taste. I opened the bag and it was a hideous Michael Kors coat. I had to hide my displeasure.

He said, "I did good, didn't I?"

My insides were screaming. *NO, YOU DID NOT DO GOOD. I told you I like purses and perfume.* He left the price tag on the coat. It was $274.00. I know dang well he did not pay $274.00 for that coat. He probably had one of his thuggish friends steal it or it belonged to someone else. Whatever the case, this coat was not my style. I gave him a hug in order to hide my displeasure and said, “Thank you.” I rolled my eyes. All the while thinking, *who can I re-gift this to?* I conveniently left the bag in his house. I went back to my car and sat down in the passenger seat. I prayed before he came out of the house. He finally came out of the house and put his bags in my car. As we headed to 20 East, I sat quietly. Remember, this is the guy who does not want to talk so I am not going to talk to him. He tried to make small talk. I responded yes or no.

“I could have stayed at home if you were going to treat me like this” he said.

“You can turn the car around. You are the one who does not like to talk, remember. Hell, I can talk to you or not. I just want to ride.”

He continued talking about his favorite subject… himself. I was not listening. I have heard the same stories since May 2018. It is now November 30th and his conversation has not changed. I was so happy when his phone rang. He talked to his best friend, brother and nephew. I talked to Bonnie and Trina. I did not have any expectations. This has been the same narrative since July. We go out of town, have big fun and then he disappears. Once we return to Fort Worth, he will disappear. I sat quietly looking at the scenery. I’ve driven up and down this highway so many times. It is nice to sit back and allow someone else to drive.

He was rather talkative after getting off the phone. In an effort to be cordial, we talked about music. We played guess the group and the year of the song. William made everything into a game. We stopped in Monroe, LA in order to fill up. After leaving Exxon and pulling back onto the highway, a rock hit the windshield on the passenger side. Dang it, this happens to every car I own. It even happened when I drove Bonnie's Honda Civic. Is this a curse or happenstance? At any rate, I called USAA in order to see if they would cover the cost which they did. I was able to schedule an appointment to repair the window on Saturday at 2pm in Pearl, MS.

We arrived in Jackson around 9pm and headed straight to E & L's BBQ. I asked if he was going to buy his own food. William usually took a step back in order for me to pay. I was not in the mood today.

"You have a free ride and free hotel room, the least you can do is pay for your own food."

He asked, "What is that supposed to mean?" I replied,

"You heard me. Are you paying for your own food? You should."

He said, "I got it. I will pay for yours and mine." I was shocked. "Thank you," I said.

E&L's is really busy, especially on a Friday night. William ordered the chicken wings; therefore, we had a longer wait. For the man who does not like to text, he spent twenty minutes texting someone. I sat facing the counter in order to avoid watching him text. I turned to ask him a question and someone had sent him a video of a young woman making her booty clap.

I said, "You are feeding that lust. I know I can't satisfy that flesh of yours."

He was startled, "Why are you looking at my phone?"

I said, "Honey, you need not worry. I'm not tripping. I cannot compete with a woman who will make her booty clap for you, nor will I try."

"My boy sent me that video." He said on the defensive .

“Sure”, I said with a smile on my face. While he was paying attention to other women, a couple of the guys in E&L’s were flirting with me as well.

We got our food and headed to the Hampton Inn near downtown Jackson. We checked into the hotel. William unloaded the car. We ate our food. My cousins Cathy and Kim texted to see what time I wanted to meet in order to decorate The Elks. We agreed to meet at 8am. William said, “I am not going because that is women stuff. I am going to the gym. Come back and get me before you go get the windshield repaired.”

I smiled. He is not going to the gym. He will be free to talk to whomever for a couple of hours. That is cool by me. I went to sleep. I headed to The Elks, and it was nice to see my family. All of us pulled together in order to clean, dust and decorate. I was looking forward to getting down tonight. We discussed the menu Ms. Shirley was catering the party. I had ordered wings, turkey and ham sandwiches, pasta, and deviled eggs. Bonnie and Larry purchased chips, dip and condiments. Cathy bought me a beautiful cake. Cathy’s friend decorated the building. We had a good time laughing and talking while we cleaned. I love being with my family.

All of them wanted to know where my guy friend was. I said, “He is at the gym.” *Lord forgive me.* That lazy joker ain’t worth a damn and is not at the gym. I hated to leave but I had scheduled the appointment to get the windshield repaired. My cousin said the people could have come to The Elks. I told her I was not aware of that, and it was too late to reschedule. I left The Elks around 1:15pm in order to swing through, pick him up and head to Pearl. It took us awhile to find the place. William called some of his relatives and invited them to come to the party. He talked to his Uncle Joseph for a long time. His uncle inquired about William’s ex-fiancée. William went into this rant about how he could care less about her. His favorite line was, “I wouldn’t piss on her if she was on fire.” He went on a tangent talking about how she cheated on him. I was thinking good for her. I would cheat too if I met someone You should be cheated on because you aren't worth two nickels rubbed together. Whoever she is did a number on him because he is not over her. She was still carrying his balls in her purse and his heart under her feet. He was not over her and it was clear in his conversation. After he finished talking to his uncle, I asked how come he won't go back to her.

"Are you crazy?" He asked.

"You aren't over her," I said matter-of-factly.

"I am over her" he said.

"No, you are not" I said.

"Well, you aren't over your ex either then," he spat back.

"Boo hoo, you, big baby" I mocked.

We finally located the building. While waiting, William and I sat outside on the bench. It was a nice 75 degrees on this first day of December. William's phone rang and he acted as though he could not hear. He said, "Excuse me, I'm going inside to take this call. My sister acts like she is going crazy."

"Sure, your sister is……," I said with a smile. I walked across the parking lot. I called my father. He and my uncle could not make it because my uncle was in a car accident and totaled his car. I told him it is well, and we will see each other soon. Tell Uncle to get well. William exited the place after five minutes. He was looking for me. I waved at him. Now he is staring at me wondering who I am talking to. It took all of thirty minutes to finish the windshield. It looks brand new to me. My Aunt Sugar and Cousin Brenda want me to come to my Aunt Minnie's house. I told William we have to go and see them.

He asked, "What are we drinking?"

"My folks don't drink like yours. You can get something to drink if you like," I responded.

"How do y'all have fun if you don't drink?" He asked.

I responded, "We don't have to drink in order to have fun. Wait until you see them, and you will understand. It is not something we do."

We made the thirty-five-minute drive from Pearl to Jackson. We arrived at my Aunt Minnie's house. We knocked and my cousin opened the door.

My Aunt Minnie grabbed me and said, "You little fast thing." I laughed.

I introduced William to everyone. My Aunt Sugar and Minnie wanted to know if he was related because our family derives from the Smiths. They discussed family origin, but it turned out we are not related. We sat there for about an hour and realized it was getting late. William wanted to go by Stamps Burgers located on 1801 Dalton Street. Stamps is known for their gigantic and delicious burgers. As much as I like to eat, I could not eat the entire burger. It was juicy and yummy. Antyhoo, we went back to the Hampton Inn in order to rest up for the night. Rest went out the window, my best friend Tina had checked into the Hampton as well. We ended up going to the Dollar Tree and liquor store. There is no rest for the weary. Tina and I had a good time walking around the liquor store. Tina is something like a bartender. She knows how to mix those drinks. Tina is the one who introduced me to Gin and 7 Up at Keesler AFB. Tina likes to drink Vodka, Cranberry and a splash of pineapple juice. The party is BYOB. I am starting to feel rushed. Ms. Shirley was bringing the food over at 6 pm. DJ Jeremiah was going to set up around 7pm. The party does not begin until 8pm. Tina agreed to go to The Elks in order meet Ms. Shirley and the DJ. I was so grateful to her. I told Tina I would try to get there before 8pm but knowing William that was not going to happen. He is slower than a woman. Just like I thought, he was more focused on getting a buzz before going to the party.

"I hate being late. It is my party and I want to be there in order to greet the guests," I snapped.

"You are supposed to be late. It is your party. I am trying to get my buzz on." His phone rang.

"Man, we are getting dressed. Y'all come on to the hotel and follow us. Everything is paid for. Come on out and have a good time."

I looked at him. I did not mind his family or friends coming but he invited them as if he paid for everything. Lord knows his broke behind did not pay for anything nor did he offer. By now, I am pissed because we are really late.

We arrived at The Elks at the same time a lot of the guests were arriving. I had to tell myself not to get an attitude. *Don't let this man's self-centeredness and narcissistic ways ruin your day.* Oh well, I am surrounded by people I love and then there is William. Upon entering The Elks, I must say the decorator did an excellent job. There was a nice background for the photo booth. My heart was full. I was so pleased. The food and cake looked great. You're only 51 once. I'm getting ready to shake, shake, shake…. shake my booty. Everyone knows I cannot hold a beat, but who cares? It's my party and can be off beat if I want to.

My Aunt Sugar, my cousins and I were having a good time. We stayed on the dance floor. I did not realize William had disappeared for a long time. His family members entered and at that point I recognized he had been missing. I hugged his family and told them to come on in and have a seat. My cousins even asked where he was. I shrugged my shoulders. At that moment, I knew he had disappeared in order to talk to one his supply. I shook my head. I was not going to allow his tacky assets to ruin my party. There were too many people in that room who loved me and who I loved. We laughed and danced the night away.

Bonnie asked, "What are you drinking?"

I said, "I am not really drinking anything because William is going to get wasted."

She said, "It is your birthday, not his."

I said, “I can dig it, but I want to get back to the hotel safely.”

She looked at him and said, “I guess you are right.”

I said, “He is full already.” I’m not putting my life at risk. I knew I would have to drive back.

William attempted to dance with me throughout the night. I was not interested in dancing with him because he was only trying to impress my family. I finally danced with him after Aunt Sugar demanded that I do so What they saw and what was were ten different things. They perceived William to be crazy about me. What they did not know is William did not give two cents about me. All of this was an act. One thing I knew for sure, William cared about what other people thought. He needed their approval. He wanted them to say, ‘look at him he is such a good man’. The little boy in him needed affirmation. The more I looked at him, the more he turned me off. His self-centeredness and pride on a scale of 0-10 was 100. The more I was around him, the more unattractive he became. How did I miss these flags? These signs were not flags, but sheets.

To say the least, all of us had a good time. It was good clean fun. We cleaned up and everyone went back to their perspective homes and hotels. William is loud and ghetto. He is even more loud after he had been drinking.

In his drunken state, “Tell your friend to come to the room with us so we can continue to drink and have fun.”

“Your loud and drunk behind need to go to sleep” I responded.

“I’m not drunk,” he said. “I’m going to call my Uncle Joseph in order to see how he is doing. You know he is 70 and he drove an hour and a half to celebrate with you.”

“I am thankful. Tell him I enjoyed him and thank him for coming.” I was in the bathroom washing my face and I could not hear his conversation because of the water. As soon as I turned the water off, William was going off about his ex-fiancée again.

I sat on the toilet for thirty minutes and listened to him rant about her. Apparently, she made a good impression on him and his family. I wish I knew her name. William has been careful never to say her name. Gosh, if I knew her name, I would call her and ask her to please take him back because he is obsessed with her. I took a shower, crawled into the bed and wondered if I will ever meet a man who loves me the way William loved his ex-fiancée. *I wonder why he will not go back to her.* With that in mind, I drifted off to sleep.

Chapter 14

On Sunday morning, I woke up to a series of text messages from my family saying how much fun they had. Tina texted to see if I wanted to go to breakfast at The Waffle House. Of course, I want breakfast. I asked William if he wanted anything. I knew he was hungry and hung over. He asked for a Tylenol or Ibuprofen and water. I always keep something for pain in my purse. I gave him an Ibuprofen and a bottle of water. I got dressed and walked to Tina's room. Tina answered the door. We hugged.

"Good morning, where is William?"

"Girl, hung over. I am going to bring him something to eat."

"He is going to need it," Tina laughed.

"Baby, William gets it in. He gets drunk every time he drinks. I have never seen him drink in moderation. Poor little thing."

We laughed as we walked to my car. We drove across the street to The Waffle House. Don't judge us. It was packed. What the hey? There is nowhere else to go in this area. Shoney's was abandoned. We found a table and decided to wait. Service was slow and poor. We placed our order, and the food arrived an hour later. We ate an All-Star Breakfast with waffles, bacon, sausage, eggs and hash browns. At this point, my cousin texted and told me that my Aunt Minnie was cooking. I'm full now. We sat and talked about old times. We talked about our days in the military and all of those shenanigans. Tina had to leave at noon and head back to Vicksburg. I grabbed mine to go order and we drove back across the street. Tina and I said our goodbyes. I went back to the room and William was awake and watching football. I gave him his food and told him I was going to visit my Aunt Minnie. He said, "I can't go. I have a headache."

"No problem," I said. I did not want him to go anyway. I am going to visit Aunt Minnie and later my Uncle Van in North Jackson.

I was wearing a black t-shirt, white jeans and black booties. As I entered my Aunt's house, I was surrounded by family yet again. Man, this feels good.

My Aunt Sugar said, "You low down scoundrel. You had us wear black and white but you wore red."

Dorethea said, "Had me out there looking for those colors but you wore something different."

"It was my birthday not yours and that is why I wore red." I laughed. Of course, they asked about William. I told them he had a hangover. Both Aunts talked about how much they liked him. I said, "That's nice". I told them we are not a couple and left it at that.

Aunt Sugar asked, "What is the problem?"

"He is not into me. So, we had to let it go."

She said, "You mean to tell me, you can sleep in the same hotel room with him and not have sex with him."

"Absolutely, he does not turn me on like that. Plus, married folks can sleep in the same bed night after night without having sex. There is no sex in the city or country either." We all laughed.

My Aunt Minnie said, "I like him."

I said, "He is nice, but I can't make him like me. He does not like me the way I want to be liked or loved. He is a garden tool and that is not what I want. Plus, he is really selfish. He pretends in front of people but is not the same behind closed doors." We dropped the topic of William and talked about old times.

My Aunt Minnie had cooked some pinto beans, yams, cornbread and friend chicken. Dang, I just ate two hours ago. I can't pass up pinto beans. I have not eaten pinto beans in twenty years. I ate a small plate of food. It was delish.

We ate and said our goodbyes. I cannot believe I forgot Uncle Van and Aunt Paula's housewarming gift. I went back to the hotel in order to get it. Upon entering the hotel room, William was still lying flat on his back. I shook my head in disgust.

William asked, "Bae, can I have some."

"Have some what?" I inquired.

"You are walking around here with those tight jeans on, and I'm turned on."

"Wait until you get back to Fort Worth and you can have all the sex you want from the women you want it from." I said with a scowl on my face.

"You and I are not a couple. We are barely friends, and I don't sex my friends."

I told him I would see him later and left the room. I hopped on I-55 North until I reached Uncle Van's house. I must say the neighborhood is beautiful. I turned down their street and into their driveway. I was impressed with the house. I loved the door. It was nice and thick. I rang the doorbell and was greeted by Uncle Van. He invited me inside and escorted me to the family room where he was watching football.

"Where is old boy?" He asked.

"Hung over and lying flat on his back."

"I figured he was because he was drinking Vodka," Uncle Van said. "I used to drink like that, but it is not worth it anymore. I used to drink and act a fool."

"I am glad you stopped. Where is Aunt Paula?" I asked.

"She is in the room listening to music."

He yelled for Aunt Paula to come up front. Aunt Paula came up front and hugged me. I bought them some wine glasses. Aunt Paula had cooked ribs, mashed potatoes and green beans. She fixed two plates for me and William. Aunt Paula gave me a tour of the house. We chit chatted for a few minutes. They walked me to my car, and I headed back to The Hampton Inn.

William was sitting up watching football. A wave of evil came over me. I'm thinking you rode for free; you are sleeping for free and now I am allowing you to watch football. I snatched the remote.

"You are not going to watch football all evening." I snapped. Tonya texted and told me about a Christmas movie coming on Lifetime.

"At 8 o'clock, I'm watching a Christmas movie," I informed him without smiling. I went to the bathroom and changed into my pajamas, played on Facebook and waited until 8pm. I turned to Lifetime and fell asleep. He got to watch the game after all.

I woke up at 7am Monday morning. I tried to go back to sleep for another hour. I couldn't sleep. Different family members began texting and calling in order to see what time we were leaving. I might as well get up and start packing. William was not good in a lot of areas, but he was good for carrying the bags, packing the car and driving. He was not going to pay for gas, but he would pump the gas.

We hit the road and within an hour and forty-five minutes we were in Monroe, LA. We stopped and ate lunch at Zaxby's. He paid for our lunch. That was a shocker. While driving back, I told him we have had some good times, but they have come to an end. We requested to go boxes, packed our food and left. While driving, we talked about all of our good times. We have gone to Austin, Galveston, San Antonio and a few other places. I shared that I wanted to continue my tour of Texas. We discussed going to

Corpus Christi in April. I love the beach. I told him that I would love for him to go in order to drive. He agreed. I looked over at my little lying William while he was driving. I wondered how many other men were like him. He discussed taking me out for my birthday.

He said, "Texas Roadhouse is a good place to have dinner."

"I have actually never been there so that would be nice," I said.

In the back of my mind, I was thinking that date will NEVER happen. We made it back to Fort Worth at 6pm. I dropped him off and headed home. He put that God-awful Michael Kors coat in my trunk as if I did not see him. I usually throw trash in the garbage, but someone would like to have this coat. I posted it on Facebook as a giveaway.

I'm on vacation for two weeks. I am going to enjoy myself. I always treat myself to a birthday dinner and movie. William called four days later.

"Hey, what do you want to do for your birthday?"

"You said you were going to take me out to dinner," I said flatly. "Okay, I will take you to Texas Roadhouse," he said. I thought to myself. *I wonder if I will have to pay for my own dinner. Probably*. I burst out laughing. I have always loved my birthday. Birthdays are special. It is the day God allowed your parents to bring you into the realm of the earth. I love to celebrate it. December 10th rolled around quickly. I dressed in a pair of boyfriend jeans, white tank, navy blue jacket, red boots and red accessories. I treated myself to The Cheesecake Factory at The Parks Mall in Arlington. William called around noon and began talking about his favorite subject….himself.

I was curt, "You aren't going to say happy birthday?" It was more of a statement than a question.

"I was getting ready to." I don't remember if he said happy birthday or not.

"What are you doing?"

"I am taking myself out to lunch."

"Who is going with you?"

"Lord knows I am ready for the day a good man will accompany me."

I enjoyed my lunch. I walked around the mall and came back home.

He called to see if I wanted to come there or for him to drive to me. His car is not in the best shape. I trust my car.

"Well, come through and pick me up around 8pm".

"Will do," I said.

Prior to going out to dinner, my back began to hurt. It was weird. The pain was not unbearable, but it was nagging. I drove to Meadbrook, and William was coming out of his house. He no longer wanted me inside of his house. He had his backpack and left his porch light on. This meant he was going to spend the night with me. William thinks he is strategic, but he wanted me to pick him up so that his car would remain in the driveway. If one of his supply drove by, he could say the light was on and his car was in the driveway which would mean he was asleep.

I hopped in the passenger side and allowed him to drive.

One of his cousins called and he had to brag, 'Aw man, I am not doing anything. I'm taking Lisa out to Texas Roadhouse because she has never been."

I'm sitting there thinking, *you aren't taking me to Paris Negro.* He was bragging as if he was doing something grand. I can afford to take myself to Texas Roadhouse. You aren't doing anything special. Just as well as William was playing a game with me, I was not innocent. I was playing a game too. He accompanied me to my party because I wanted a date. I am going out to dinner with you on my birthday because that has not happened since 1999. *Honey, I'm writing a narrative and you are a part of it.*

On the drive to the restaurant, I told William my back was hurting. The pain had come out of nowhere. He kept talking as he normally did. He never acknowledged my pain. He lacked empathy for others. We arrived at Texas Roadhouse and were seated immediately. He was talking to the waiter. I figured he wanted them to sing happy birthday to me. We sat and talked. At that moment, the staff brought out a makeshift bull for the guy at the next table. He was celebrating his birthday too.

"I bet you told the waiter today is my birthday. I'm almost positive they will be here soon," I stated.

"Nah, why would I do that?" He laughed. He is such a liar. He lies for no reason. We ate a juicy steak, corn and mashed potatoes. The food was delish. Thirty minutes later the bull arrived. I'd told this ninja my back was hurting. I was vexed but I am not going to embarrass myself. I will play along. It was kind of fun sitting on that makeshift bull but all I wanted to do was go home. He paid for dinner, and we left the restaurant. Early in the situationship, William would open the car door for me. He soon stopped. Now he only does it in front of an audience. Remember, he needs the approval of others. As we walked to the car, there were a lot of people leaving the restaurant. I knew he was going to open my door because he needs people to believe he is a wonderful man. He is predictable whether he knows it or not.

We went back to my apartment. I could not wait to take off those heels, put on pajamas and take a pain pill. We sat on the sofa. All of a sudden, alerts began going off on his phone. I smiled. I encouraged him to answer because nothing was going on between us. I told him the alerts sounded like the one from the dating site where we met.

He began lying. "I am not on a dating site. I sell items online and it makes a ding when someone looks at an item. You are paranoid and jealous."

"That is the lie you want me to believe. It makes you feel good to tell your little friends that I am jealous and paranoid. You and your friends are pitiful."

He began texting but he hid the phone on the other side of his leg. He was trying to act as if he was not texting. Dude, I am looking at you. I felt sorry for the women. He was going to love to bomb those women and discard them like he did me. It was all fun and games to him. He got high off of texting multiple women while he was with me. It fueled his ego.

I thanked him for taking me out. I asked him to text the video of me on the bull so I can post it on Facebook. He could not text it, so he had to send it in Messenger. After I uploaded the video, I made sure to block him. I did not want him having access to me on social media nor did I want to see any activity on his page. My phone lit up and it was Monica. She must have seen the video on Facebook. I did not answer the phone because I did not want to hear the hope in her voice.

She left a voicemail. "Hey, happy birthday. It is me. Who took you out for dinner? Call me back. I want details. Bye".

She will have gotten excited about William taking me out for my birthday and will have us in a relationship.

William asked, "Who was that? Your man?"

"I wish I had one. You would be the first to know if I met one. FYI: that was your favorite cousin. I cannot deal with her false hope as it relates to your raggedy assets. She will have us in a relationship, and I just can't tonight."

He did not respond. He looked at me. I turned and went to the bedroom. I said my prayers and went to sleep. I had a doctor's appointment at 1pm on December 11th. It worked perfectly. I dropped William off at home and headed to my appointment.

I did not reach out to him again. Early on, he groomed me into believing he did not celebrate pagan holidays. Therefore, I was not interested in playing a cat and mouse game for Christmas. It's not that he does not celebrate holidays, that frees him up from buying gifts. If he is with one supply, his defense can be that he does not celebrate holidays. It's all game. Christmas came and went. He called and we talked briefly on December 31st. He reached out to me on January 2, 2019.

"How was your New Year" he asked.

"It was good. Yours?" I responded. Before we could get into a conversation, his phone rang.

"I have to go." He abruptly hung up.

Chapter 15

January 3, 2019

Lisa's text: You are a joke. You are incapable of loving anyone other than yourself.

William's text: I love you.

Lisa: You might but I require loyalty and fidelity. I can't be with you. I desire a full commitment to me and forsaking all others. Is it fun hurting and playing games with women? Does it make you feel special or happy? Is it fun laughing at women with your friends and family? I'm curious as to how you feel when you strategically set out to play women.

William: Stop it baby. Stop it I will do better.

Lisa: We can be friendly but no more trying to date. I am pissed off at myself for allowing you to talk me off of that dating site. You begged me to be in a committed relationship. I knew you were not the faithful type. You tried.

Between January 3 and January 13, 2019. He called multiple times.

January 13, 2019

William: Will you answer the phone, please?

Lisa: You don't like talking to me.

William expressed wanting a relationship. He acknowledged screwing up and begged for another chance. I discussed his confession with Monica, Brittany, Tina and Bonnie. Tina said she supports my decision whether I give him a chance or not. Bonnie did not have much to say either way.

Lisa: Dude I know you said you would do better. I just don't trust you. You lie too much. You are a whorish man. I am not willing to ignore that.

William: I'm sick of this bullshit. Leave me alone.

Lisa: Sure thing.

On, January 26th, I needed new software.

I called Brittany, "Man, my computer is going haywire. I am trying to work on my book. This thing is going crazy. I don't have the money to take it to the Geek Squad. I hate to call William."

Brittany said, "Call him anyway. This is business."

"I do not want to open a can of worms," I continued.

"His prices are cheaper than the Geek Squad." Brittany said, "Call him. If he says no, then so be it but I am sure he could use the money."

January 26, 2019 @ 4:40pm

Lisa: This is business, not pleasure. I need assistance. I will pay full price. Thanks.

I texted Brittany and told her he probably won't respond. Brittany said he would.

January 26, 2019 @ 6:50pm

William: I will do it. No need to pay me.

William called around 7:30pm. No manners whatsoever.

He immediately stated, “I bet I know what is going on with it. I will install a new program” he explained. I asked, “Do you want me to drop it off or meet you halfway somewhere?”

“I will come and get it” he said.

On January 28, 2019 @ 12:16 PM

I’m cooking Let me know when you are on your way.

William arrived around 1:30pm. I opened the door, and I knew he was hoping that I would jump up and down with excitement. One thing I noticed; he was on the phone. Second thing I noticed, he was skinnier and unattractive to me. On this day, it is safe to say he was very unfortunate looking to me. I said hi, the computer is right there and went back to the kitchen. As usual he was on the phone with one of his boys. I continued to cook.

Thirty minutes after entering my apartment, He says “you sure aren’t happy to see me”.

He made this statement while on the phone. Mind you, the last time we saw each other was December 10th.

“It’s a new year and you are doing the same thing. You walk in with your rude behind talking on your phone as always. Ever since I met you, you are always on the phone with your boys. You are so rude. Every time you came to my apartment, you are on the phone. I was never a priority to you. No, I am not happy to see you with your pitiful self. Just sad. Sad and tired I say.” He told his boy that he would call him later. If you are wondering if it was his boy, yes it was. I could hear his voice. He talked to this friend daily and multiple times per day. I began to wonder if William was bisexual. His phone rang and rang. He looked at the caller ID, but would not answer. His phone rang non-stop. He turned it face down but it continued to ring. As I was walking to the kitchen, his phone rang. I heard a woman's voice. He said, "I will call you right back". He hung up quickly.

He was working on the computer when "The Steve Harvey Show" came on. He and his friend hate Steve Harvey.

"You hate him because he told the secrets of you men people" I said.

William said, "I don't like him because he has been married three times." "Who is he to talk about relationships?"

"He is perfect to talk about relationships because he has experienced the worst and now, he is transformed". I continued. "You don't have to like him. I do. Steve is a mirror, and it is difficult to look in a mirror. Steve said a man will change for the woman he loves. Steve used to be a garden tool, but he was transformed by the renewing of his mind. Plus, he finally matured and became a man".

I was looking at him right smack in the eyeballs. He said, "And you are listening to him." You women are so gullible?"

"Clearly, I fell for your lies in the beginning. Shots fired. Seriously, dude. You have said I am wonderful and all of this good stuff. But you can go months without seeing me, weeks without talking to me, so ninja, I am not the woman for you. You made no behavioral changes in the six months I have known you. Well, all of your changes were negative."

He arrogantly turns to me and says, "You have never caught me with anyone have you?"

"I did not try to catch you. One thing about you is you don't go out on dates, you invite women to your home, cook for them or hide out in their homes or apartments because you do not want the risk of running into one of the many women you are sexing. You think you are slick but you are not. You are a typical wounded and broken Black man. Your mom and dad abandoned you and you have not healed from those wounds. You like so many brothers are broken".

I went to the kitchen and grabbed a bag of skins. I returned and plopped down on the sofa.

He said, "The white man got y'all messed up. You are eating slave food. These white folks done messed y'all up. I eat clean."

"Well, you eat clean, but the effects of the white man have trickled down to our relationships. The reason you and so many black men are whorish is because the white man taught y'all to look at us as an object and not a person or human being. Master raped us, beat us, separated us and helped to split the family, and this has trickled down generationally. So, when you think that you are being smart and have it all together, Master has affected your ability to see the Black woman is a Queen deserving of respect and fidelity." He sits and stares at me.

His phone rang but he answered this particular call. I heard a woman say, "Hey".

He said, "Let me call you right back."

He abruptly hung up. He had done that to me so many times. I told him you might as well talk to her. He lied, "It was a robo call."

"Lord man, you aren't going to tell the truth if Jesus gave you the opportunity to enter heaven. If Jesus said tell the truth William and you can enter the kingdom, you will still lie. We are not a couple. So, handle your business."

Shortly after that phone call, William said, "I have to go. I have a customer getting ready to stop by." He left rather quickly.

The following day, William requested the picture we had taken at my birthday party. I had deleted him off the picture. I just wanted my computer. Of course, his needs were the priority. I had to wait until after the Super Bowl. On February 4, William called and told me he was going to bring the computer. Later that evening, he told me to come and get it. Mind you, I have not been inside of his home since October. I had been begging for my belongings since October. I texted and asked him to have my stuff packed up.

I arrived at his house around 7:45pm. He had most of my stuff on the table. I noticed someone had used my Orange Blossom body wash and vaginal wash. There were only three bottles of body wash. All of my toothpaste and deodorant were gone.

"Where is the rest of my stuff? I had more bottles of body wash, several tubes of toothpaste, and deodorant."

I did not ask but walked to his bedroom and began packing my stuff. I grabbed my make-up bag, Fenty beauty products, and flat iron. I went to his bedroom, and he followed closely behind. I grabbed my slippers from beside the bed. I grabbed clothes out of his closet.

"I did not know you had clothes in my closet."

"Of course, you did. You are the one that told me to leave these very clothes."

I grabbed my pajamas out of the drawer. He pulled some of my pajamas out of the top drawer on his side.

I said, "Really, why are my pajamas moved? You gave me this left top drawer and all of my stuff should have been in there. Did you let someone sleep in my stuff? Come on man."

I threw those pajamas and loofahs in the trash. He said, "That is what rich people do. Just throw stuff away."

"I'm funny that way. I don't know who and how many slept in my pajamas." My Daisy by Marc Jacobs was still on his dresser but no one had touched it. He helped me to carry all of my items to the car. I said goodbye. Once I arrived home, I did not have room for any of the items. I tossed all of the slippers and pajamas in the trash can and took it to the dumpster. I did not want any of the items. It was mine and it was the principle of the matter.

William began calling almost every day. On February 12, he began telling me how I complained too much, was too insecure and was not satisfied with anything he tried to do for me. I listened all the while thinking ninja you have not done anything except take me to Boomer Jack's and Texas Roadhouse. I can afford to take myself to any restaurant in the DFW area. Pay attention…this is the discarding phase. This is where the narcissist blames the victim for everything, and he lets you know how horrible you are. He went on and on about how horrible I was. He thought I was different than the others. I was what he was looking for in the beginning and now he is not sure. I was watching "The Wendy Williams Show" which means I was partially listening. I heard him but not really.

I tuned back in and heard him say, "I was turned off especially when you came banging on my door. I never thought you would do anything like that."

"I know you care what people think but I am not going to keep apologizing for that night. I know you were embarrassed and will NEVER get over that incident and that is because you were in the house that night. Peace."

I hung up. This fool sends a text: *I love you.*

He does not love me, and I know that for a fact. He does not love himself. He confessed his love for me and his desire to reconcile in that text. He asked for another chance to make things right.

Valentine's Day is fast approaching and according to William it is a pagan holiday. He called on February 12th. I decided I would taunt him. I don't celebrate Valentine's Day either but what the hey?

"Hey, I miss you. What are you up to?" he asked.

"Oh, I'm excited about the gifts I am going to get on Valentine's Day," I said coyly. He threw a tantrum about not celebrating pagan holidays.

I said, "I believe in compromise so if you are not willing to buy me a gift for Valentine's Day, then we don't need to try again." I ended the call.

My big sister, Felisha called. "Hey, is William going to spend Valentine's Day with you?" she asked.

I replied, "He does not celebrate Valentine's Day."

"That is because he is whorish and that is game," she inhaled and continued, "He is going to be 70, wearing a diaper and hoping someone washes his nasty behind."

Brittany and Monica also called to inquire about our possible Valentine's Day date. I told them the same thing I told Felisha. Brittany said, "I believe he is going to come through with some flowers, candy or something, especially if he wants to get back with you."

"You know he is broke. I can buy my own candy and flowers."

"But it is the thought that counts. It is a day of love."

"Me, technically Valentine's Day is a pagan holiday if you do your research."

"You are sounding like him," she said.

"No, I have actually done my research on all holidays, and he is accurate as it relates to ALL holidays being pagan. It is not to agree with him, it is not biblical but us Christians have gotten caught up in all of these traditions," I said. "At any rate, I will not be moved whether he shows or not. I have been single most of my life. Plus, I know where I stand with him." Brittany, like Monica had hope. In my mind, I thought about the scripture that the elect will be fooled. Last year, Brittany had a dream that he bought a ring and would propose around Christmas. She'd had a dream that we were going to be together, but it was just that…. a dream.

On February 14, 2019, William came over carrying a backpack. I figured he had a gift in there. The size of the backpack let me know the gift was small and cheap. He went straight to the bedroom. I had purchased him Vodka and cranberry juice. He appeared shocked.

"I was not expecting anything."

"I know. I'm thoughtful like that."

"Hey, will you go in the bedroom and bring me that backpack please?"

I went into the bedroom and saw this ugly cheap bear and $2.99 box of candy lying on the pillow. I rolled my eyes. I can't wait to throw this mess in the trash. My sister Toni doesn't call me Erica Cain for nothing. It's show time. I squealed with joy.

"Oh, you shouldn't have. Is this for me? I'm so excited?"

I ran back to the living room acting like I had won the lottery. I gave him a hug. While hugging him, I rolled my eyes and asked God to forgive me. He asked if I cooked. Absolutely not. I had eaten before he came. I am not feeding him. He asked if he could watch 48 Hours. I wanted to watch Law & Order: SUV. Since I am hospitable, I allowed him to watch 48 Hours. I sat on the other end of the sofa, wrote in my journal and texted Bonnie. His phone was ringing off the hook, text messages and alerts. His phone rang and rang and he was getting more and more tense. Every now and again, he responded to a text.

He said, "This is my brother."

He began texting 'his brother'. Come on now. I was joking but serious, "You have not texted your brother since I have known you. You always talk to your "brother".

I told him he was going to be in trouble because the others are going to wonder where he is on Valentine's Day.

"You will escape their wrath because I know you have told them that you do not celebrate Valentine's Day. They will feel special on the 15th, 16th, and 17th." I burst out laughing.

I watched him hide his cell phone while texting. He was responding to text messages when he thought I was not looking. When he went to the bathroom, he took his phone with him. When he went to the kitchen to fix a drink, he turned his phone face down. I was thoroughly entertained watching him think he was smarter than me. He really believed I did not know what he was doing.

I became bored with his antics. I got up and said I am going to the bedroom in order to watch Law & Order SVU, and finish writing in my journal.

"Don't leave. Stay in here with me. I miss you when you aren't around," he said.

"You don't miss me. I don't miss you either. I am tired of watching you struggle. Go ahead and text your lady friends in peace. Good night." I set the alarm.

William crawled into the bed around 10:15pm. He did not touch me, nor did I touch him. I fell asleep around 11:30 pm. The following morning, William left for his morning run. As he turned to leave, the man repeated his favorite line "I will call you later." I stared at him but did not respond.

I did not hear from William for at least a week. During this time, my cousin introduced me to one of his friends, Calvin. We began chatting back and forth. William also resurfaced. I was in constant communication with him and Calvin. William called and heard noise in the background.

I said, "My 4-year-old grandson is visiting from California, and we are playing."

He said, "That is so cool. I am going to buy him something."

"Don't do that" I said. "I can tolerate your lies, but you are not about to play that emotional mess with my grandson. If you come over here, you best come with toys in hand."

He said, "That is what I am going to do."

Calvin called daily. I lost interest in him after he told me he had two children under 13. That is a no, for me. The following Sunday, Calvin invited me to dinner at Applebee's. We agreed to meet after church. While at church, William texted and said he was coming over later with my grandson's toys. I said that is fine. I arrived at Applebee's for my "date". We greeted each other out front. Calvin was shorter than I would like. He opened the door and we were escorted to a booth. Calvin had two cell phones. One was his business phone. He took business calls throughout the "date." I did not care. I was enjoying my food. William texted and said he would be over shortly. I told him I was on a date and would be home later. Of course, he thought I was lying because his response was 'quit playing.'

Calvin had recently ended a long-term relationship with his son's mother. The relationship ended two weeks ago. I told him he was not ready for a relationship, but he is ready for a sexual encounter, but I would not be his bed buddy. I encouraged him to take some time to heal before jumping from hole to hole. He claimed he was over it and his son's mother. I looked at him and smiled. I knew he was lying too. Men move on quickly, but they are still attached to their exes. Dinner ended and he walked me to my car. I headed home knowing I would not see Calvin again and nor did I want to. Once I arrived home, my children and grandson came over. We watched the NBA All Star game together. William came over three hours later. He brought my grandson a football and some racecars. As soon as he sat down, he turned his phone face down. I smiled.

He noticed my face was made up.

He said, "You don't wear a lot of makeup. What did you do today?" "I met a guy for dinner." I answered.

"No, you are not that type of girl."

"What type of girl? I'm not in a relationship with you. I can date just like you can. Don't think I was being faithful to you. I just could not meet anyone. I will not date one guy ever again unless God says Lisa this is the one. Other than that, I am going to date who and when I want."

It felt good to look him in his eyes knowing that I wasn't sitting around waiting on him. Although I was honest with him, he did not believe I had gone out on a date. In his mind, he is the only man in Fort Worth and all of us belong to him.

William loved to tell me that I talked to his boy Rico. I don't know who Rico is but William swore that I had dated him. I know who I date and talk to. Rico is not one of them. William continuously accused me of flirting with Rico on a dating site. William was trying to play mind games. He was trying to manipulate me into getting off the dating site because he did not want me to see him on there. He was trying to wear me out with false accusations. He said he has not been on the dating sites in months. Every other word was Rico said he saw you on the dating site I wanted to scream….. *you broke, lying azz negro…you are Rico. You are on the dating site.* Gosh, he is so pathetic.

Chapter 16

One night I could not sleep. I read my Bible, prayed and still could not sleep. I decided to browse the dating site. As I was scrolling through pictures, the headline displayed "People you may want to meet". As the picture scrolls by there goes William. He posted one of the pictures I had taken of him when we went on vacation. He had changed his profile name to ManofGod01. I scrolled through his page. He had been back on the site. Although I was off the site, he last viewed my page on January 4, 2019. He had been on the dating site the entire time. I screen shot the picture and sent it to my sister, Leslie. I laughed and laughed. I sent him a message on the dating site.

The message read:

Hi, ManofGod01. You have lied and lied on Rico. I knew you were still on this site. His profile said he needs love. I started laughing and said out loud, 'you need to learn how to love buddy.' I left my profile up for one week, but he never responded. I know he got the message because those alerts will notify you.

It is now March 2019; I was preparing for my trip to Corpus Christi. It was a trip he and I had planned. Well, I make the plans and he go along for the ride. I do enjoy his driving. It is the one time I get to sit back and relax. I told my aunt that I was going out of town next week. My Aunt Sugar said, "Take my boy with you. I do not like you on that road by yourself."

"I might because I am tired. I hate to cancel my trip."

Aunt Sugar said, "Take him with you. It won't hurt anything."

I do like William as a friend, but we never should have tried to date. I told Leslie I was going to ask him to go with me.

"He will go. I'm almost positive he will drop whomever and drive you," Leslie said.

"We are not going as a couple. I do not expect him to drop anyone but he is going to have to lie about his disappearance for a few days. Plus, my aunt wants me to take him so I will not be alone," I explained. "Girl, how do you know he is dating someone else?" she asked.

"He cannot be alone. He is hyper-sexual. He is with someone or sometwo or somethree," I said. Both of us screamed with laughter.

"Girl, you are too silly. I'm with your aunt. Ask him to go. You don't need to go by yourself."

Eight years in a city and I do not have any friends. I long for the day that I will meet a good friend who can ride with me. I do not want to ask him to go. I asked my children, but they do not want to go.

Dear God,

I have been asking for a friend for years, but no one has come along. I do not want to ask William to go but I do not feel like driving by myself. I drive all of the time for work, and I get tired. I want to relax sometimes. God, when will I meet a like-minded friend? When God? Why don't I have any friends I can call? This is going to fuel his ego. Lord, I have been praying for one good friend for seven years, but no one has manifested. I do not want William to be my only friend. Well, he isn't a friend. He is actually a frenemy. William does not know how to be a friend to anyone. He bad mouthed everyone behind their backs. William has manifested into Derek. Both are good on the surface but mean spirited to the core. They feel superior to everyone around them and that is why they bad mouth everyone, even those they claim to love.

Uggghhhh, it pains me to reach out to him. His ego is big enough. I can unblock his number and call him, but I do not want to do that right now. So, I wrote William a letter.

March 22, 2019

Dear William,

I hate to ask you this but…….! I would like you to accompany me to Corpus. I would like you to drive. So, you have a week a two to get your alibi together. If you are interested in going, text me I will unblock your number within the next couple of days.

I called Leslie. "Girl, why aren't you here?" I need a friend. I told her I opted to write him a letter.

"He is going to go with you. Heck, buy some condoms and get laid. There are not any good men out there so you may as well have sex with him", she said.

"Absolutely not. Condoms cannot protect me from that filthy penis. I am good not having sex. I am good my friend", I said.

On March 26, 2019, I received a text from William.

William: When are you going to Corpus?

Lisa: April 4th next Tuesday.

William called, "Are you still acting funny? You had my number blocked."

I answered a question with a question. "Who is acting funny? I do not want to bothered with you, we're not dating anyway."

He said, "You should not do that. You should not block me because you do not have any friends in this area, and I can help you out."

I fired back, "You are lazy. You don't know how to do anything. You don't know how to change a flat, wash a car, mow a yard or anything. What can you help me with outside of offering me sex and driving me out of town? You don't have anything to offer outside of a penis." William, "Girl, you are so crazy. I miss you. I'll go with you."

On March 30, 2019, 3:37PM, I texted Leslie

Lisa: Hey lady. He is going with me.

Leslie: I knew he would go. He loves you.

Lisa: That boy has all of y'all fooled. This is a free trip. He is incapable of loving anyone.

On April 1, 2019

William: Do you still want me to go with you?

Lisa: I want you to drive.

William: Okay

Lisa: I can pick you up Thursday at 9am.

William: When are we coming back?

Lisa: Saturday or Sunday?

William: Okay

April 4, 2019 @ 8:32 am

Lisa: Are you awake?

William: Yes.

Lisa: I'm leaving out in five minutes.

William: Okay.

William was sitting on his porch when I arrived. He was trying to make sure I did not come inside. He said he would be right back out. Although I had to use the bathroom, I did not say anything because he was going to lie. Honey, we are not a couple. I hopped on the passenger side and waited for him to come outside. I stare at the house and think how much I used to love coming over. Now, I do not want to enter that home any more than he wants me to.

Bonnie called, "Good mornting. Are y'all on the road?"

"We are getting ready to go now," I replied. "He is getting in the car now".

Bonnie said, "Hey, William."

"Hey, Bonnie," he said.

"Girlfriend, I cannot wait to get to this water."

We chatted for a while longer. We said our goodbyes. I stared out of the window overlooking the scenery. "So, you aren't going to talk?" He asked.

"What do you want to talk about?", I asked. I continued, "You are not big on conversation. I will just follow your lead. Whatever you want to talk about. I will oblige."

William talked about everything and nothing. We made the six-hour drive to Corpus, checked into the hotel, changed clothes and walked downstairs to the beach. I had reserved a beach front hotel. I love the beach. We actually had fun. The USS Lexington was to the right of the hotel. I wanted to take a tour of the ship. I have always wondered what it was like on those Naval Ships. We planned to do that tomorrow. We had dinner at the hotel's restaurant and bar. The food was not that great. We laughed and talked. I fell asleep.

The following morning, we got dressed and made the short walk to the USS Lexington. It cost $16.95 to take the tour. I paid for myself and entered the ship.

"Bae, I cannot believe you are not going to pay for me. I don't have that much money."

I turned and he was actually having a tantrum, "I cannot believe you. I am not where you are financially."

"I am not paying for you. I am tired of you trying to get over on me. Go back to the hotel."

He bought his ticket but looked at me in disbelief. I shrugged my shoulders and walked off. He shrugged off his anger because he could tell I was unbothered. The tour lasted almost four hours. We went up to the flight deck, took pictures in airplanes, took a tour of the sleeping quarters, infirmary, and mess hall. The stairways are steep. Now I understand why most sailors have bad knees. We ate a light lunch and actually had a pleasant time.

We went back to the hotel, took showers and found a restaurant with the biggest burgers. We ate and made plans to go to South Padre Island the following day.

William asked if we could have sex. "Fool, are you serious? What vibes am I giving off that suggest sex? I am not flirting with you. It is two days, and you cannot go without sex. There will be plenty of partners to have sex with in, Fort Worth, I said."

"I want to have sex with you," he said unfazed.

"You can't be serious?" By the look on his face, I knew he was serious. "I am positive you are having all the sex you can stand. You are not going to be faithful to anyone are you?"

"What are you talking about?" He asked. "I am not seeing anyone," he said. "You cannot be alone." "Oh, you can abstain, but I can't." "Absolutely not hoe. Yous a hoe (in my Ludacris voice)," I laughed. "You lack self-control. You can't go more than 24hrs without sex. It is not an addiction. It is lust and no connection to Christ," I said half laughing and half serious.

"You think you are funny," he said.

One of his friends called. He had him on speaker. He said, "I can't believe Lisa thinks I am hoe. Am I a hoe?"

He quickly removed his friend off speaker. I shook my head. I changed into a bathing suit.

"I'm going to the beach," I said.

"I don't want you going to the beach alone. I am your protector. If something happens to you. I would feel responsible for you." "Nothing is going to happen to me. I have angelic protection, but you don't know anything about that." I grabbed my cell phone, hotel key and left.

We dressed for dinner. After dinner, we went to Walmart in order to buy a cooler, bread, cold cuts, chips and drinks in order to take to the beach tomorrow. That night, I read a book while he talked to his boys and watched television.

On Saturday morning, I woke up excited. I heard the beaches in South Padre were gorgeous. We ate sandwiches for breakfast, packed the cooler and hit the road. It was so much traffic leaving Corpus, but the drive was beautiful. I am actually glad he drove because we rode across the causeway and all I could see was water. I will drive across long bridges when necessary but today I am thankful.

We found a secluded spot on the beach that had a covered bench and table. It was a perfect spot for a picnic. William wanted to sit where there was a lot of people because he needed to be seen. He needed the attention of others. He wanted to be a part of everything. I want to sit on this beach and watch the waves in peace. Overall, it was a nice time. I got tired of him asking for sex. Can we just enjoy the moment? We stayed at the beach most of the day. Every now and again, William would ask if I was happy to have met such a handsome guy. He is not the best-looking man I have dated. I have dated several attractive guys. He is so full himself. You are not that good looking. Calm down brother. You look okay.

Chapter 17

The drive back to Corpus was nice. We packed our bags, took a shower, ate dinner and went to bed. The following morning it was raining hard. William packed the car and we headed home. I informed William that I was having outpatient surgery on April 9th.

He said, "I will drive you."

I said, "No thank you because you are always late and unreliable. I cannot miss this appointment"

"I would not do you like that," he said.

"I don't think it is intentional. You just can't help it," I frowned.

"Let me know if you need me to take you," he said.

"I appreciate the offer, but I got it," I said. I dropped him off at his house and headed home.

On the day of the surgery, I did not expect to hear from William.

He called the next day, "Hey, I am repainting my living room. Me and my nephew are doing the work. It is going to be so much better. I need to change the colors. It has been like this since that last relationship. It has been time for a change."

He went on and on talking about himself. I began talking out loud. "Oh Lisa, I am glad the surgery went well. It is nice to have someone check on you. Do you need anything?"

"Oh no. I didn't know you were having surgery."

His phone rang "I have to go. I will check on you later."

While on Instagram, I saw a post from Gina da Silva:

Somatic narcissists are obsessed with their bodies and their looks. They are sexually hyperactive and use their body and sex appeal to obtain lots of narcissistic supply. They often have multiple sexual partners, all at the same time. This makes the somatic narcissistic feel powerful, irresistible, and smarter than their victims. Should their victims find out, the narcissistic will lie and deny, cry some fake tears, love bomb, but he/she will never change, same tactics, new victims, that's all.

-They boast heroic acts (that in fact never happened);

-They pretend to have very deep spiritual beliefs (their behavior/actions prove otherwise)

-They say that they are very successful

-They take credit for other people's achievements or ideas

-They tell outlandish stories

-They say that they are financially stable or that they are wealthy

-They say that they are faithful.

April 10, 2019 @ 10:37 PM

I screenshot the message and text it to him. I told William this is all of you. I know this will not register with him, but I could not help it.

Narcissism is a real disorder. Satan was the first narcissist. Narcissism is rooted in pride. Two narcissists five years apart. Someone shared a post on Facebook about staying away from narcissist men. Is it possible to stay away from men who are narcissist? My son from another mother commented, '*All men are narcissists because of our egos. Some men are abusive, and some are laid back. In my opinion, I do not think you will find a man who is not a narcissist. I have narcissistic tendencies, but I also have a loving heart and is forgiving. Some narcissists are extreme.*

I have to agree with him. I have spoken with many women whose husbands presented with symptoms suggestive of NPD or Narcissism Personality Disorder. Some women prayed and saw a positive changes year into the marriage. Other women are still praying and believing a change will come.

Many people do not believe God speaks to them outside of reading the bible. I believe differently. I believe God speaks through other people, ministers, television, radio and social media. God speaks through whomever He pleases. On this day, God was speaking to me through Facebook live. On Memorial Day, Dr. Tamarrah Tarver was live. Her topic was Mental Health Monday and the ever popular Narcissistic Personality Disorder. I grabbed paper and pencil in order to take notes. Per Dr. Tarver, they shift blame. They never do anything to anyone else. One of the traits of a narcissist is compulsive lying (Derek and William). They are highly gifted in the area of lying. They are skillful in lying. They have an inflated since of self-importance. Grandiose thoughts of self, disregard feelings of others, God complex (it's all about them). It is a mental disorder. They believe they are the only ones who are important (William). Narcissists have troubled relationships. Behind the mask, there is fragile self-esteem. That individual has low self-esteem.

OMG, this is William and Derek. Both presented with such high self esteem, but I knew that was a false sense of high self-esteem. Both struggle with low self-esteem. Many people think women are the only ones who suffer from low self esteem. Come through Dr. Tarver.

More symptoms:

-Pre-occupied with fantasies about success.

-Take advantage of others in order to get what they want.

-They are manipulative.

-They pick out someone who is supply.

-To a narcissist you are not a person you are an object.

-They do not have the ability to care about other's feelings.

-They do not have a moral compass.

-They have difficulty regulating their emotions.

Narcissism is linked to four things:

• Genetic Predisposition- there are inherited characteristics that come from the person's genes.
• Neurobiology-there is a connection between the brain and behavior. At first, they think a certain way and then act out.
• Environment-mismatches in parent-child relationships. In their childhood whenever they experience negative behaviors this is when their behavior forms. It stems from parenting styles whether overprotectiveness or neglectful parenting.
• Narcissism is more common in men than in women.
• Be envious of others and believes others envy them.
• They have a hard time maintaining and sustaining relationships, not just romantic but all relationships. It is their way or the highway. They suffer with extreme depression and anxiety. They battle with suicidal behaviors.

Three Phases of a Narcissistic Relationship:

• Idealize Phase-the beginning of the relationship they love bomb you. They don't look at you as people. They look at a person as supply. The Narcissist has chosen their supply. If you are appealing or an empath you are a great supply for a narcissist. This is the beginning. They are going to love bomb you. They are going to worship you. They will text you every day. Immediately, they are going to tell you that you are the one. They want you to think they are perfect. They will go above and beyond. It's not genuine. They are going to tell you that their exes are crazy. They won't tell you that they cheated and lied to their exes. It's only a matter of time before you become the ex that was crazy. This is the phase where they are on an emotional high. If you are the supply to that narcissist, this is something they have done to every woman before you. Everything a narcissist does is methodical. Same script-different character. They will text you because they want you to be stimulated. You are thinking they love you. This phase lasts a few weeks to a few months. They can only put on that mask for so long.

In hindsight, William love bombed me. He started off complimenting me. He wanted to spend all of his free time with me. He called, texted and reached out all day every day. He cooked for me. He did everything he could in order to show me that he was into me. That lasted from May –July or maybe mid-August. The love bombing phase was brief. I continued listening.

• Devalue Phase-Once the masks fall off the real person begins to surface. In this phase, once the relationship has gotten its rhythm, they began to devalue you. They do it with emotional, verbal or physical abuse. It starts out subtlety. They begin making comments about it is better women out there for me. I don't like this or that. They are trying to break you down. They are emotional vampires. If you have a big heart and an empath, you are a victim of a narcissist. You will need counseling. You will have PTSD, paranoia and anxiety. If you are a Christian, you will want to pray for the relationship. However, they do not want to work on the relationship. They will talk down to the supply. The person who praised you at one point, you will realize they are not in your corner. They are actually your enemy. They have a way to make you look crazy and unstable. They can get other people to believe what they are saying. They go on a smear campaign. They will make you think you are insecure. YOU ARE NOT INSECURE. This is the methodical behavior from the narcissist. This makes the narcissist feel better about themselves. The more pain they inflict on their supply-it fuels their ego. They are psychologically abhorrent. They will begin to withdraw their affection from their supply. They do this tactic so you will become needy and co-dependent. They will start blaming the victim for everything. They are already getting new supply. They can devalue you because they are already in Phase I of love bombing someone else or multiple supply. Narcissists are serial cheaters. They do not like to be alone. **They will deny they are cheating**. They will **NEVER** take ownership. A narcissist will **never** say they are sorry. If they do, they do not mean it. They do not have the capacity to be sorry. It's their ego. The truth is they are who they are.

I continued putting the puzzle together. William began to discard me in August to October. He would reel me in and throw me back out to sea. He had me on the hook and then toss me off the hook. It was a game of catch and release. He resurfaced and disappeared. He began blaming me for the problems in the relationship. He never assumed accountability for anything.

• Discard Phase-they will throw you away. They completely remove themselves from you. They don't need you anymore, especially if you have seen the real them. They do not want anyone to see them. When the supply asks them for compromise, peace out. It's not in them to be honest. A narcissist does not have the capacity to love purely. They only love themselves. They will be in a new relationship and will get married quickly. The new supply thinks she got him. They both will become obsessed with you. The new supply is being told lies. The narcissist is going to throw his ex under the rug. They will say she is crazy. They will not say they cheated. They recycle their exes. The ones they say they can't stand; they go back to their ex-wives, fiancés and girlfriends. They love control. If the new supply thinks he will never go back to his ex, you are mistaken. He is probably calling and texting the ex. They keep all of their supply separate by putting bugs in their ears so they will never come together. He is telling everyone the same thing. It is a game. A narcissist will try to turn back to anyone they had a relationship with. They deem you as an object. If one supply is not working for him, he will immediately discard and have a new supply. Narcissists use ghosting as a technique. When they discard you-they go ghost. At this time someone else is receiving attention from the narcissist. Narcissists don't have the ability to love you. They will not answer their phone or text. Their attention is elsewhere. You are hurting but they do not care. The victims blame themselves. The part that keeps you connected to the narcissist is called trauma bonding. You don't want the relationship. You want the part of the relationship where you feel loved. You fell in love with the representative. During the love bombing phase, they draw you in and they want you to want them. Your brain craves that same feeling that you had during the love bombing phase. Narcissism is a Cluster B Personality Disorder. It is a disorder that is characterized by someone who has unpredictable behavior, unpredictable thinking and over dramatic tendencies.

You can put William's picture in the DSM-5. He love bombed, discarded, devalued and ghosted me. Over and over, I told him he was incapable of loving me. When he began ghosting me, he would say that I wanted to sit up under him every day and that was a lie. That is the story he was cultivating for his smear campaign. When I went to his home in October, he was with someone then. He spent Thanksgiving Eve and part of Thanksgiving with me and my family. He spent the rest of Thanksgiving with someone else.

Four Types of Narcissist;

• Covert Narcissist-closet narcissist and are subtle. They are more reserved. They are the most dangerous. They are monsters. They appear to be humble and shy. Play victim or a martyr. It's an act. They are methodical and manipulative. They are passive aggressive.

• Overt Narcissist-they are more blatant in their behavior. They demand admiration. They love to be flattered by others. They love admiration from other people. Anytime something does not go their way, they have tantrums. They look at you as an opponent, not a teammate. They will be in competition with you.

• Cerebral Narcissist-extremely intelligent and extremely intuitive. Jezebelic if you will. They possess high intellect. They use their intellectual prowess and superiority in order to impress others and illicit praise. Their intelligence makes them feel empowered.

• Somatic Narcissist-soma means body. They are obsessed with the body. It's about physical aesthetics and sex. They are hypersexual. They are risky as it relates to sexual behaviors. They will sleep with multiple partners without protection. They have a god complex. They feel empowered by their penis. They will their victims in through the channels of sex. They understand the power of sex. Sex is one of the most powerful acts of intimacy. They will give their supply a sexual experience so they will never leave. Everything is centered around sex. Zero accountability. They will have sex with one on Monday, two on Tuesday, three on Wednesday. If you have the ring, the somatic narcissist does not have the ability to be with one person. If they are married, they are going to have multiple affairs. If single, they do not practice safe sex. They sleep with multiple women.

A wave of fear has come over me. I had unprotected sex with him in the beginning. I called my doctor for an appointment. I need to be tested for every sexual transmitted disease. I am so happy I decided not to have sex with him anymore. God forgive me. I am so happy I chose me over my lust of the flesh. William fits all of these categories. He plays coy and a martyr in the beginning of the relationship. He is definitely passive aggressive. He loves to be admired. Every time we went out somewhere, he would stick his chest out around women. He would try to get women to look at him. He needed the attention from women. He wanted people to say how handsome he is. He even talked about how handsome he was on a regular basis. He is highly intelligent. He loves to hear himself talk. He really thought he was impressing me with a lot of his knowledge. He works out religiously. He is obsessed with his looks. He is obsessed with the way a woman looks. He thinks he is perfect and he wants the women he dates to be perfect too.

Techniques Narcissist Use:

• Mirroring-when they first meet you. They mirror what you do. If you say you love going to the beach. They will say, so do I?
• Smear-the moment they discard you they will make you look crazy. They will ruin your name. They are compulsive liars. They are charismatic and believable.

****Narcissists hate being exposed. They will put it on you before they are found out. ****

• Gaslighting-distorts another person's perception of reality. It makes you think you are going crazy. They will not admit cheating. They talk in circles and bring about confusion.
• Hovering-when they are done with another supply. They try to suck you back in. They will give you a few weeks. They will wait awhile before they try to love bomb you again. It will start with texts or email. They will beg you, but it is not genuine. Once they have lured you back in, they go and hover the other person in. They get off on this technique. It is a game. They don't have the ability to love. They want you back into the vicious cycle. A narcissist will NOT change.
• Triangulation-one of the most common tactics of all narcissists. A narcissist has multiple supply. They cannot be alone. They love people to fight over them. They will play all sides. It's a love triangle. They will create jealousy amongst other people. They will tell you their ex wants them back. They create drama. They will tell all parties(supply) they love you. A narcissist loves chaos. They cannot function in an environment of peace.

The Grey Rock Method-this method encourages a narcissist to lose interest in you. When you have to interact with a narcissist do not show care or concern. Be unbothered even if it is negative because they want a response.

No Contact Method- block them from everything phone and social media. Remove everything that reminds you of the narcissist because they always feel like they can re-enter your life. No contact is the best way to get free.

Have a strong support system. You were broken down in the discard phase. Never jump into a relationship after dealing with a narcissist. You have to heal. You have to be around affirming people. Be around positive people. Maintain a healthy prayer life.

William mirrored me in the beginning. If I said I did not sleep around, neither did he. If I said I had a specific standard, so did he. He was like a parrot. He really came off as a good man. He often referred to himself as a good man. That is how I knew he was lying. A good man does not have to promote himself. It is reflected in his actions. Dang it, that one impulsive night in October gave him the ammunition he needed. That gave his story a semblance of credibility. I am slightly touched but in a good way. He is the crazy one but it has gone undetected.

William cannot hover because we do not have the same circle of friends. He cannot get in touch with me because I blocked him. I was never his friend on Facebook, and I made sure of it by blocking him early into our situationship. I can remember William telling me that his ex was hanging around his family. One day he asked if I would fight over him. Absolutely not. He would respond by saying he was joking. I knew he was serious.

Regardless of the information I shared, the same women kept urging me to give William another chance. Ms. Roberson even told me she had a dream that William got delivered from his perverse spirit and we were going to get married. Ms. Roberson told me I have to stop calling him a whore. I have to pray for his deliverance. She said I cannot talk about him and pray for him. I do not see this man in the spirit realm. Sometimes the things that are seen in the spirit does not manifest for years to come. I am not willing to wait on his deliverance.

When I considered giving him another chance, God stepped in. On this particular day, I had driven to the office. Brandy and I pulled into the parking lot at the same time. Brandy is the fiancé of one of William's friends. We greeted each other with a hug. I knew she would not say anything, but I had to. "Hey lady. How are you? You know William and I did not make it," I said. "I heard. He was talking to my boo on yesterday and asked if I had seen you," she said.

"He was too whorish for me. I do not want that community penis around me," I said laughing but seriously.

Brandy said, "He will not do right by anyone. He keeps multiple women but always blames the women. I know he is the problem in all of his relationships. You did right because you were going to catch something from him."

"He need not ask about me because I do not ask about him at all. I require loyalty, fidelity and integrity which he does not possess," I said. She said, "He is so whorish, and he is getting too old for that mess. He needs to sit down somewhere." We laughed and went our separate ways.

On three separate occasions, I have been told that I was going to get married to my God ordained husband by the time I turn 52. Well, I will be 52 in December. Folks, prophecy in part and in flesh. A part of me hopes the prophecy will come to pass but I have to be okay if it doesn't. Two weeks ago, Ms. Roberson called to tell me that God was going to deliver William. I said, "Yeah right." It's not that I doubt God. I doubt that William wants to change. I thought people have to want to change. William does not believe he has a problem. So, I am not holding my breath. Last week, another Prophet said that the guy I had dated was going to apologize and want to reconcile. If he does not do right, God would send someone else. Per the Prophet, "If he comes back and has changed do not rule him out, but if he comes back with the same behavior accept his apology and move forward. God knows how to send someone better."

One month after this prophetic word was spoken over my life. I had a series of missed calls. It is not uncommon for me to get a lot of robo calls. Shortly afterwards, a text from a strange number popped up.

Chapter 18

June 14, 2019 @ 12:33 PM Text Message

Brandy: Hello lady, how are you? This is Brandy. We spoke about a month ago. Just reaching out to say hello and I had an important message for you when you have a moment this is my number and please give me a call when you get a chance. This is urgent.

My heartbeat was racing, my palms were sweaty, my stomach was in knots because I do not know what she was trying to tell me. Immediately my mind went to the negative. She was calling to tell me William was HIV positive and to go and get tested. I got a complete work up and all of my results were negative. I had a panic attack. Dear Lord, Sweet Jesus breathe Lisa. Breathe. Jesus, I don't want a disease. I repented and have not had sex since 2018. I know it is only one year, but I am trying. I hope this woman is not calling to tell me that this man has got a disease.

I prayed before dialing her number. My hands were shaking. I had to drink a bottle of water. While the phone rang, I was rocking back and forth like Ms. Sophia from "The Color Purple". She answered. "Hello, how are you?" I asked.

"I am good. William was talking to my boo last night and he asked me to call you. He begged me to call you. He said he wants to do right by you and that you are a good woman. I told him I do not want to be in the middle of anything and please do not have me call this woman and you don't do right by her."

"I don't know Brandy. He was too inconsistent. I had his back, but he was not there for me. He was not faithful. He lied all of the time. I just don't know if I want him back. It bothers me that he gets to lay around with different women and then want to come back," I said.

"He got dogged out by some of those women and now he realizes that women are out there playing the same game as men. He said he knows you are a good woman," Brandy said.

I continued, "I just don't know. Something is not right with him. I told him not to pull me into this madness, but he did. He disappeared too much and would not return my calls. I have to think about this. I'm tired of players. I don't understand why it is so difficult to be faithful."

"He is getting too old. He did say that everyone has someone except him. He said he was ready to settle down and get married," Brandy continued. "I told him do not disturb this girl if you do not want her. Me and Bae told him you were nice. He kept saying he screwed up." "I have to pray about this because this is scary. Tell him I will think about it."

I hung up and had mixed emotions. I don't know. I just don't know. Is this a part of his game? Is he sincere? He is a narcissist. Did the other supply get boring, and he is making his rounds? Narcissists love to hover and circle back to the same women. I cannot stand the risk of another counterfeit relationship. I will not be a part of a concubine. I just don't know but I do want an apology.

I continued working. I called Leslie and caught her up to speed. "Girrrlllll, I love your love story. This reminds me of Hosea and Gomer except William is the whore. Maybe his lovers are not around him anymore and they are leaving him in the dust." We howled with laughter.

I said, "Girl, I am so confused. I think about the prophesies, but I also think about William the man. He was less than honorable. I do not know if I want to experience that level of disappointment again." "Unblock him and see what he says. I'm rooting for the both of you. You two look like you belong together. You two look like a God ordained couple, tall and regal. The two of you remind me of Barak and Michelle. Remember I told you the first picture you sent I noticed both of your body languages. It was awkward. But the more time y'all spent together, you could see the beauty and growth in your relationship. I am a sucker for love. I want this to work," Leslie said.

"I don't know Leslie. I just don't know. This is nerve wrecking because he disappointed me," I explained.

I concluded my workday. I drank a bottle of wine and fell asleep. I woke up at 2am. I decided to unblock William. I sent him a text.

Lisa: Brandy told me you wanted to talk. I have unblocked your number.

I watched television and drifted back off to sleep. On Saturday morning, I woke up at 7:30am. I read my word, worshipped and was grateful for another day. I decided I would give William until 12noon. If I have not heard from him, I will block him. Of course, I knew he was not going to call by noon because that is typical of him. I decided I would run errands. I turned on praise and worship music, took a shower and got dressed.

I hopped in my car and headed to the beauty supply store. I need to get my weave redone because I am going to Monroe for my sister/cousin's reception. I need to look fresh. It's not about me but I still don't have to look like Raggedy Ann by the head. So, I will stop by the beauty supply store on Lancaster. I purchased my hair and walked around Citi Trends. I looked at my phone and it was 12 o'clock on the dot. I blocked William's number. I hopped in the car and decided to go to Henderson's Chicken in Duncanville. While driving, another strange number came through, but I did not answer.

June 15, 2019 @ 12:41pm

Text Message From Unknown

Teresa? Hello this is William's friend. Can you please unblock him he received your text at 2 am but he was asleep and did not get a chance to call you. Please call him thanks.

June 15, 2019 @ 1:09pm

Text Message to William

Lisa: I am not waiting all day for you to call me. You got five minutes, or I am going to block you again.

William called immediately. "Hey, how are you?" He inquired.

"I am good," I replied.

"What are you doing?" "I am out in these streets," I said. He was making small talk. I interrupted.

"I am not in the mood for small talk. Say what you want to say," I demanded.

"I want to apologize for what I did to you. I am sorry. I miss you and want to see you," he pleaded.

"Um, no you can't see me," I said.

"I did not do right by you," he revealed. I'm thinking no shit Sherlock.

I was able to unleash everything I had been holding on to.

"You are damn right you did not do right by me. I was there for you and had your back. You were disrespectful during entire relationship. When we went to R. L's Blues Palace you were talking to a girl right in my face. You texted and talked to women while you were at my apartment. You switched out my body wash for someone else's. You let someone use my body wash and deodorant. You would not respond to text messages and disappeared for months. Remember when we went to Corpus? I asked you who was that woman on the picture. You said it was your niece but on the drive to Corpus you did not know who she was or what picture I was speaking of. I have never heard you talk about a niece before. You are evil. I cannot do this. The more I talk the more I realize you were not a good person at all."

"I am sorry about all of that. I still do not know what picture you are talking about," he lied.

"You have that many nieces that you don't know their names," I said sounding incredulously.

"Oh wow, because if the shoe was on the other foot. I would be able to say that is my nephew Deandre, Robert, Shaun, Victor Jr, Darius, Lil Robert, Brandon or Byron but you have no idea who your nieces are." I did not want to tell him that Brandy already confirmed he had been with multiple women. I just needed to let him know that I saw everything he did but I did not have the energy to argue at that time.

"I am sorry. I am apologizing for everything and hope you can forgive me," he said.

"I forgave you a long time ago. You cannot help that you are a whore," I spat.

"I am not a whore. I am a good man," he said.

"Maybe one day you will be the good man you have told yourself that you are."

He said, "You are a good woman, and I was an asshole. I want to see you."

"I cannot right now. I am not sure you are sincere." I started thinking about Dr. T's teachings about narcissist and how their apologies are never sincere. It is a game to re-earn their supply. I stopped daydreaming and he was still talking. I don't know what he said but I did hear him ask if he could see me today.

"Absolutely not. You don't get to trick off and I come running." Another trait of a narcissist is the inability to be alone. I wonder if something went south with his last supply and now, he is circling back around.

"Hey, I appreciate your apology because I know that is not who you are and I do forgive you but I cannot take the chance that the same problems we had in the past will be a part of our future. You do not like talking or texting, but I still require that."

"I promise. I am going to do better. Just give me a chance," he pleaded.

I cannot get excited because he was begging and pleading. Men beg and plead all of the time but still have multiple women. I think we should be friends because he is incapable of loving anyone other than himself. When I don't know what else to do, I pray. I arrived home and went straight to my knees.

"Father God in the name of your son Jesus. I do not do well in relationships. I have bad track record with men. I do not want to date another counterfeit. I can forgive but this is confusing. I do love him but he has shown me the worse already. God, help me. You know I believe in love, forgiveness and will throw common sense out of the window. I cannot allow him to use me or manipulate me. I need to know if he has been delivered and is sincere or if he is on demonic assignment from the pits of hell. I do not want my peace disturbed. I cannot have peace disturbed. I will not have my peace disturbed-in Jesus Name. Amen and Amen".

Of course, I call my circle in order to tell them that William called and apologized. A couple of them were excited. I told them to calm down because an apology means nothing if it is not supported by changed behavior.

Chapter 19

June 1, 2020, at 8:05 AM

William: Hey Bae. I just wanted to say good morning. Call me when you get up.

June 1, 2020, at 11:21 AM William: Are you ignoring me?

June 1, 2020, at 11:23 AM

Lisa: Not ignoring you but you are not a priority, and I will no longer rush to respond.

June 1, 2020, at 11:25 AM

William: Don't be like that. I am trying to do better.

William called, "Hey Bae. What are you doing?" "I'm working, you?" "Missing you." He lied. "Seriously, you do not have any friends around here. You may need me to help you with your car or moving furniture or you may need a ride or something," he stated. I snapped, "With friends like you, who needs enemies. You don't know how to change a flat or work on cars. You are too "fine" to move furniture. You can't do anything but talk. I can pay someone to do the things I need. I can call Uber if I need a ride. You want to be friends withal of your exes because you need them more than we need you." "Oh, hursh," he said. Oh, hursh, was a phrase he used when he did not have a comeback.

June 3, 2020, at 9:00 AM

William: Have a good day at work. I just wanted to let you know I was thinking about you.

June 5, 2020, at 4:10 PM

Lisa: Hey

William: You are acting funny.

Lisa: No, we teach people how to treat us. I taught you to treat me like I did not matter so all is fair.

William and I danced around for a few weeks. He invited me to come by his house and do laundry one Sunday afternoon. When I pulled up to the house, I texted and asked him to come outside in order to help with my laundry. I had taken my work computer as well.

When he came outside, the first thing he says is "Look at you, acting like you are not happy to see me."

I said, "It is nice to see you, but I am not thrilled to see you anymore than you are thrilled to see me."

I was thinking this boy is an extreme narcissist. As we entered the home, I noticed a woman's touch. I decided not to compliment the new additions. He offered to put my clothes in the wash, but I declined. I am not impressed by this act of kindness. Because I know this is simply an act. I loaded the wash, sat down and proceeded to work.

"You have not seen me in a long time and now you are focused on work".

I said, "Yep. Work pays the bills"

"You didn't miss me?", he askedH. OMG. This dude needs validation. "Dude, you want every woman in Fort Worth to miss you?" I asked. I continued, "Sheesh dude. You are doing too much."

His phone rang and he talked to one of his boys. He wanted me to know that it was a guy. He leaned over so that I could hear a man's voice. I do not know why he is performing because we are not getting back together. Several phone calls came through and that was the William I know. He had this inflated sense of self.

He felt important getting all of these phone calls. He laid the phone face up beside me. I shook my head. William doesn't know that I am aware he has blocked all of the other female's numbers while I was there. He would lie to them later.

"Hey, let's go and get something to eat."

We went to Stormie Monday's and got oxtails, cabbage, rice and beans. The food was excellent. I did notice that William never acknowledged my presence. My son called and I did not acknowledge William's presence either. After hanging up, William asked if I told my son, I was at his house.

"Why didn't you tell him you were with me"? He asked.

"The same reason you did not tell your brother and nephew I was with you," I said.

"We are each other's secret." He looked. I know he was not accustomed to me being combative. Hey, I have minimal respect for you and the more I sit beside him, respect is going from minimal to non-existent. As I was typing, I could see him watching me.

I asked, "What are you looking at?"

"I was looking out of the window". This was his way of demonstrating some level of interest but all I saw was a slithering serpent. Serpent he was....Serpent he is. As he was staring at me, I was thinking all I want him to do is connect my electronics. I do not want to be his friend. He does not know how to be a friend. Everything with William is an act. "Are you going to treat me like that when we get married", he asked. "I am not going to marry you. I do not need the problems you are offering," I scowled.

"You are going to be my wife," he said matter-of-factly.

"That would be a no. You really think talking marriage is winning me over. Bless your little heart," I said half smiling and half frowning.

June 11, 2020, at 2:00 PM

Lisa: How are you? How much do you charge to connect electronics?

William: I won't charge you. What do you need done?

Lisa: I need to buy another printer and get it connected to my new laptop.

William: Go to Walmart. It should have some affordable printers. I can come and hook it up this weekend.

On Friday morning, I went to Walmart in search of a computer. To my surprise, the shelves were empty. I asked one of the employees if there were printers in the back. The young lady conducted a search and returned with an apology. Dang it.

I called William. "Hey, how are you? I am at Walmart and printers are out of stock," I said.

"You got to be kidding me? What is going on?" he asked. "I just had a thought. The children will be homeschooled, and college students will be going back as well. What was I thinking?" It was rhetorical.

"I am going to check a few more stores," I said.

"Let me know if you find anything, if not I will look on my side of town," he offered. I drove around to several more stores and could not locate a printer.

June 12, 2020, at 5:00 PM

Lisa: I could not find a printer.

William: I will look on my side of town. It should cost about $100 for a decent printer.

Lisa: You want me to be your wife but can't pay for the printer.

William: You aren't my wife yet.

Stingy bastard I said out loud. I sent $100 via CashApp to William. I figured his cheap assets could pay the taxes.

June 13, 2020, at 5:00 PM

Lisa: Hey. Did you find a printer?

William: Yes. I have located one.

Lisa: Will you be able to connect it on tomorrow?

William: Yes.

Lisa: Come after 2pm, please. That will give me a chance to enjoy service.

William: Church? Online?

Lisa: Yes. I watch service with my Bible and pay attention as if I am there. No disturbances are allowed during that time.

William: Okay. See you tomorrow.

I turned on worship music, prayed for peace and anointed the doorpost, furniture and anything he may touch. I cannot afford to have those demonic spirits lingering in my apartment. On Sunday, I enjoyed the word Apostle brought forth. I had this feeling in the pit of my stomach that William was not going to come through. Around 4pm, no William. I rolled my eyes and prayed before calling.

"Hey., what time are you coming over?" I could tell he was driving. At that point, I knew he had probably taken someone out to lunch or dinner with the money I sent him. "Oh, I did not find a printer". "What? You texted and said you'd located a printer".

"I called Walmart and they said it was some in stock. I went to pick it up, but they were gone."

This mother……. Don't get mad at him. He is who he is. I took a deep breath.

"Are you there?" He asked. "I will order it from Amazon on my business account. It will be here by tomorrow. I have an Amazon Prime business account." I hung up. I cried because I was angry at myself. This mofo has spent my money. I can feel it. I wonder if he treats all of his costumers like this or was it just another stab at me.

Monday came and I hated to reach out to him. I waited until that evening before I called. "Hey, did you order the printer?"

"Oh no, I did not get a chance. I talked to a friend who said I can use his account at Sam's Club. I will go and pick it up from there."

I inhale. "Are you in a place where you can hear me?"

He answered, "Yes. I am home. I am washing dishes."

"You know. I tried to be supportive of you as a man. I tried to have your back. I tried to show you what support, friendship and love looked like. I had your back. I would have done anything for you. I asked you to write your vision and make it plain. I understood and did not judge your financial situation. I allowed you to use me and take from me. You thought you were getting over on me. You were not. I allowed you to ride my coattail because I wanted your company at that time. When my family friends assumed you were paying for the trips, I remained silent. I did not put you down. That is what a solid person does but you do not know what that it is because you are not a solid person. You have never been in love with me nor do you know what love is. You don't know love. Whatever your mother did not give you, that is what you keep looking for in women. Society loves to say women have daddy issues but men have mommy issues. You lack integrity. You lack character. You tried to criticize me but your comments were fictitious. It was a part of the narcissistic "devaluing phase". I am not devaluing you. I am speaking from the heart. When you allow the truth of who you are to surface, when you accept that you are broken and wounded, when you accept that sleeping around with multiple women is a sign of brokenness, when you recognize that being a player is juvenile… you will make someone a good man. Men like you try to sell the "good man" image. A lion does not have to say it is a lion….it shows. Your continuous self description of a good man is you trying to make someone believe you are better than you are. One day you may catch up to the prophecy you have spoken over your life. You have good qualities, but you are horrible. I would not marry you. I would probably have an affair. You do not know how to make love. You fuck. You bang. Banging lacks intimacy. You like to hit it from the back because that keeps you disconnected. Sex is a release for you and punishment for the woman. Minus making a woman laugh, you do not have anything to offer. I feel sorry for you and men like you. I feel sorry for myself for wasting time. I feel sorry for the women you have met and will meet. You are their problem now. I don't regret meeting you but I never want anything to do with you ever again. You lie so much. The only way you will be that good man is if God guts you out like a fish and clean you up. Until then, you are a lost individual. You actually hate women and see us as property. I used to wonder how easy it was for men to move on, but it is easy. You, narcissist people are not connected to anyone. Every woman you meet won't have herself anything but a headache. You were an asshole in the situationship and now you have taken my money. I bought and sold your cheap behind for $100. Goodbye." I deleted and blocked him for good this time. I was done entertaining every prophetic voice concerning him. I was done entertaining my hope for his change. I was done believing that love can change a person. I was done believing that my kindness can cause a person to want to be with me. I was done listening to the circle give me false hope regarding another human being. I was done.

Monica called, "How is it going?"

I sighed. "It is going good. I waited before I told you that William had wanted another chance because I did not want you to get excited. I gave him another chance and he proved to be what he is. I cannot believe I was so stupid."

"Don't call yourself stupid. He presented to be this person that you could love. The heart wants what the hearts want. You want love and there is nothing wrong with that. He is the one who played himself, not you. He took advantage of your ability to love and forgive. I am sorry." I was sincere by saying, "It is not your fault. I listened to you and Brittany, but it was my decision to stay in that mess for as long as I did. I won't do that again. I have to deal with the consequences of my actions, not you or anyone else. I have to pick up the pieces of a broken heart not the people cheering me on. I cannot afford to silence the still small voice that speaks to me. God revealed this man to me early on, but I allowed the voice of others to draw his voice out and now I have to go through the deliverance and healing from all of these arrows. Me. Not any of you. I will chat with you later."

I started thinking about all of the prophetic voices. Ms. Roberson had dreams of us getting married and William being delivered. Brittany saw him in the spirit praying and asking God to give him another chance with me. She also saw a vision of him begging God for me to be a part of his life. Monica consistently justified William's behavior and saw only the good parts. She often dismissed my feelings. Leslie felt good about us together. I do not know if Leslie was hearing from God or if it was her emotions and her desire to see me in a relationship. I also wondered if they were laughing at me behind my back. Were they pushing me out there only to make fun of me and relish in my pain? I would hope that is not the case. I would hope that my circle of friends does not secretly hate me and want to see me suffer. If so, that would be cruel. I really pray that it is not the case.

I hate to see women go through the emotional rollercoaster of heartache and disappointment. It is emotionally draining. I will never encourage my friends or family to stay in a situation that is detrimental to their spiritual, mental or emotional well-being. I gave him multiple opportunities to be a good man and friend. He failed miserably at both. I gave him the opportunity to demonstrate integrity in business. He took my money.

I recognize that I am not responsible for my pain but I am responsible for my healing. You would think that I would be afraid to love again after William and Derek. I am not afraid of a new love but I am afraid of the pain associated with these past experiences.

It is amazing that so many voices have so much to say but no one was accurate. Two years ago, my publisher said by the time my book hit the shelves, I would be attending a book signing with my husband. That did not happen Of course, 52 has come and gone. I am almost 53 years old. I am still single and fabulous. I am living life on my own terms. I learned that I was not dating from a healthy place. When you date from a healthy place, you immediately recognize the monster before you. You recognize that you are single, but you do not have to settle.

I know what you are thinking. You are thinking that meeting someone online is desperate and unconventional. I disagree. You nor I are Ruth gleaning in Boaz's field. You nor I are Rebekah offering water to our potential husbands or their camels. You nor I are Esther. No one is throwing parties in our honor in order for us to meet a King. As society changes, so has dating. Places you may meet someone have changed too. If you are hoping to meet a man at church, it's probably not going to happen. The men you meet at church has probably slept with most of the women at the church. Can you say awkward? On the other hand, most of the men in churches are married, gay or both. If marriage is the goal, how do you plan to meet someone? Besides, no one other than the UPS man is going to knock on your day.

I'm still a proponent of online dating. You have to vet the person online just like you would the person on the pew. "Unmarried men and women: If God's will for your life is salvation, yet He won't choose salvation for you what makes us think He will choose mates for us? He will always suggest, but He won't ever decide. Who you choose is ultimately your call"-David Burris.

In the future, I will follow Michael Baisden's advice: Ladies, stop allowing men to take you off the market privately when they are still on the market publicly.

Any man that will uncover you before the wedding night, he is not your covering. The fact that I slept with William early in the relationship was a huge red flag. I was able to identify that I too struggle with the lust of the flesh. My decision to stop sleeping with him was the best decision I ever made. I have been abstinent for two years. Yay God. I have learned the importance of self control. I desire a husband who possesses this characteristic as well. Until he comes, there is absolutely no sex in the city.

References

Dr. Aesha. (2018, December 14). AspireTV, Single for the Holidays w/Dr. Aesha, Déjà vu Dating: How to stop choosing The Wrong Partners. Retrieved from Facebook Live http://www.facebook.com.

David Burris (2020, September 17) Permission to Think Differently Retrieved from Facebook http://www.facebook.com.

Fatal Attraction, created by Jupiter Entertainment TVOne, 2013-2020.

Gary Chapman (1992) *Five Love Languages*. Northfield Publishing

Larry Flint Retrieved from en.wikepedia.org.

Steve Harvey (2009, May 23) Oprah Winfrey Show, created by Oprah Winfrey, WLS-TV Chicago(1986-1988). Harpo Productions(1986-2011).

Steve Harvey (2009) Act Like a Lady Think Like a Man. p. 292.

Hugh Hefner Retrieved from en.wikepedia.org.

Nicole Moore(2017, December 22). Dating For Growth vs. Dating For Outcome, Love Works. Retrieved from http://www.youtube.com/c/NicoleMoorelove.

Gina da Silva(2019)Narcisstic_abuse_lifecoach Retrieved from Instagram Post.

Scandal, created by Shonda Rhimes, Shondaland, ABC Studios, 2012-2018.

Tim Clinton and Gary Siboy. *Why You Do The Things You Do?,* pp. 8-9.

Tamarrah Tarver(2019, May 31) Mental Health Monday. Retrieved from Facebook Live http://www.PRETTYGIRLWORLD.ORG.

CPSIA information can be obtained
at www.ICGtesting.com
Printed in the USA
LVHW050455200122
708789LV00010B/314